PRENTICE HALL
LITERATURE

PENGUIN EDITION

Teaching Resources

Unit 4
Poetry

Grade Ten

PEARSON
Prentice
Hall

Upper Saddle River, New Jersey
Boston, Massachusetts

ISBN 0-13-165372-5

1 2 3 4 5 6 7 8 9 10   09 08 07 06 05

Contents

Part 1 Read Fluently

The Poetry of Cornelius Eady

Poetry Collection: Maxim Pushkin, Federico García Lorca, Elizabeth Bishop, Rudyard Kipling

Poetry Collection: Denise Levertov, William Carlos Williams, Robert Frost, Naomi Shihab Nye

Poetry Collection: Ki Tsurayuki, Minamoto no Toshiyori, James Weldon Johnson, Dylan Thomas

Poetry Collection: Priest Jakuren, Ono Komachi, Theodore Roethke, William Shakespeare

Poetry by Gabriela Mistral, Gwendolyn Brooks, John Keats

Part 2 Paraphrase

Vocabulary Warm-up Word Lists

Study these words from the poetry of Cornelius Eady. Then, complete the activities.

Word List A

equivalent [ee KWIV uh luhnt] *adj.* equal to or same as
   The Tahoe ski vacation package is <u>equivalent</u> to the Reno ski package.

principles [PRIN suh puhlz] *n.* basic rules, laws, or truths
   Our math class studied the <u>principles</u> of geometry last year.

renowned [ri NOWND] *adj.* famous; well-known for a particular reason
   In our family, my aunt is <u>renowned</u> for her onion soup recipe.

slight [SLYT] *v.* to ignore or treat as unimportant
   The film's special effects are so great that critics tend to <u>slight</u> the actors.

sympathy [SIM puh thee] *n.* sharing someone's feeling
   I felt <u>sympathy</u> for the injured runner because I have had a sprained ankle, too.

uncouple [un KUHP uhl] *v.* disconnect; unfasten
   They need to <u>uncouple</u> the engine from the rest of the train to fix it.

Word List B

application [a pli KAY shuhn] *n.* the process of putting something to use
   The gas engine shows one <u>application</u> of the laws of physics.

expectation [ek spek TAY shuhn] *n.* a looking forward to
   Our <u>expectation</u> is that the movie will be very entertaining.

foundation [fown DAY shuhn] *n.* basis; base
   Our house is built on a cement <u>foundation</u>.

inertia [in ER shuh] *n.* the tendency of matter to stay at rest
   A soccer ball remains in a state of <u>inertia</u> until you kick it.

laboratory [LAB ruh taw ree] *n.* place for scientific research
   A science <u>laboratory</u> must be kept free from germs.

practical [PRAK ti kuhl] *adj.* useful; functional
   Paper clips and staples provide <u>practical</u> means of holding papers together.

Name _____ Date _____

The Poetry of Cornelius Eady
Vocabulary Warm-up Exercises

Exercise A *Fill in each blank in the paragraph with an appropriate word from Word List A. Use each word only once.*

It was late at night in the housing project. Nearly all the lights were out. Paula was hard at work on her model trains. Her collection had grown so huge that Paula had become [1] _____ among collectors. Her passion for her hobby was almost an obsession. She did not mean to [2] _____ her schoolwork, but it just did not hold her interest the same way. That night, she was trying to [3] _____ a caboose from a train. She gave a hard tug, and the [4] _____ of physics ensured that the force snapped the train into two pieces. The caboose was bent. As I walked in, Paula looked upset and I felt [5] _____ for her. This broken toy was the [6] _____ of a broken heart to Paula.

Exercise B *Revise each sentence so that the underlined vocabulary word is used in a logical way. Be sure to keep the vocabulary word in your revision.*

Example: Wet sand makes a sturdy <u>foundation</u> for many buildings.
Wet sand would make a very weak <u>foundation</u> for a building.

1. You will be quite surprised if your <u>expectation</u> proves correct.
   _____

2. A helicopter is a <u>practical</u> way to get to school.
   _____

3. One <u>application</u> of a calculator is predicting the future.
   _____

4. I knew the room was a <u>laboratory</u> because I saw a stage and curtains.
   _____

5. A basketball bouncing in an empty room is an example of <u>inertia</u>.
   _____

The Poetry of Cornelius Eady
Reading Warm-up A

Read the following passage. Pay special attention to the underlined words. Then, read it again, and complete the activities. Use a separate sheet of paper for your written answers.

In 1960, one song changed popular dance forever. Before that time, partners danced in one another's arms. Then, Chubby Checker released his version of "The Twist" and the <u>principles</u> of dance changed almost overnight. The song presented rules for partners dancing without touching. Across the country, dance partners began to <u>uncouple</u>, taking a few steps apart to twist the night away. In the world of popular dance, this change was the <u>equivalent</u> of the invention of the car in the world of transportation.

"The Twist" took off after Checker performed it on *American Bandstand*, a popular music television program that launched many hit songs. "The Twist" reached number one on the musical charts on September 1, 1960, and it soon became a dance craze. The energetic movements were simple but fun. Here is how many twisters described the dance: Imagine drying off your back with a towel. At the same time, crush out imaginary ashes with both feet.

The song became more <u>renowned</u> when it was released in Great Britain in 1961. It re-entered the music charts and quickly regained the top position.

"The Twist" brought fame to Chubby Checker, but it also limited his career. Fans were so eager to hear his signature tune that they would often <u>slight</u> his other abilities. "In a way," he once commented, "'The Twist' really ruined my life. I was on my way to becoming a big nightclub performer, and 'The Twist' just wiped it out. It got so out of proportion. No one ever believes I have talent." Many musicians felt <u>sympathy</u> for Checker's situation. Others might have felt jealousy, wishing that they could have had such a monumental hit.

1. Circle a word that is a synonym for <u>principles</u>. Then, tell what *principles* are.

2. Underline the words that tell how partners began to <u>uncouple</u>. Then, describe something else that might *uncouple*.

3. Underline the words that describe a change that was <u>equivalent</u> to the change caused by the twist dance craze. Explain what *equivalent* means.

4. Underline the words that tell what happened because the song became more <u>renowned</u>. Then, describe a musician who is *renowned* today.

5. Underline the words that tell what fans would <u>slight</u>. Then, tell what *slight* means.

6. Circle the words that mean the opposite of feeling <u>sympathy</u>. Then, describe an event that might make you feel *sympathy*.

Name _____   Date _____

Read the following passage. Pay special attention to the underlined words. Then, read it again, and complete the activities. Use a separate sheet of paper for your written answers.

Dear Wonderful Wanda,

I desperately need your help because I give the worst dance parties on the planet! Whenever I throw a dance party, my friends stand in the corners looking about as happy as mice in a science <u>laboratory</u>. I might as well decorate the room with test tubes and hand out white coats. What can I do to help my guests get over the horrible <u>inertia</u> that keeps them stuck in one place?

Dear Pitiful Parties,

Do not buy those white coats just yet! Wonderful Wanda is here to help turn your dance disasters into runaway successes. With the <u>application</u> of my helpful hints, you and your friends will be dancing until you drop.

First, it is important to create a positive and accurate <u>expectation</u>. Let everyone know that your party will include dancing. Create an invitation that uses catchy song lyrics and pictures of dancers to give your guests a good idea of what to expect.

Do not forget your <u>practical</u> preparations. Make sure you have enough room to dance. Move furniture and lift up rugs to create a smooth, hard surface. Check your sound system to make sure it is in good working order.

As you know, getting people to start dancing can be the biggest problem. You need to help your guests overcome their shyness. A great way to get people up and dancing is with a few quick lessons, so consider asking a friend of yours who knows a new dance to come and teach the steps to your guests.

A good mix of music is the <u>foundation</u> of a successful dance party, so choose a variety of songs and styles. Let the mood of the room guide the songs you choose as you switch between up-tempo dance hits and slower, romantic songs for couples.

1. Circle the words that describe things in a <u>laboratory</u>. Then, tell why a *laboratory* would not make a good setting for a dance party.

2. Circle the words that describe <u>inertia</u>. Then, tell what *inertia* is.

3. Underline the words that tell what will happen due to the <u>application</u> of helpful hints. Then, tell what *application* means.

4. Underline the hint that tells how to create an accurate <u>expectation</u>. Then, describe an *expectation* you have had that turned out to be true.

5. Underline one example of a <u>practical</u> preparation. Then, give one *practical* piece of advice to help new students adjust.

6. Underline the words that name the <u>foundation</u> of a successful dance party. Then, describe what you think is the *foundation* of a good dance song.

4

Cornelius Eady
Listening and Viewing

Segment 1: Meet Cornelius Eady
- What did Cornelius Eady come to understand about jazz that changed the way he approached writing? Why might poetry be an effective way in which to convey personal stories?

_____

_____

_____

_____

Segment 2: Poetry
- Why does Cornelius Eady use repetition in his poetry? In your view, what does Cornelius Eady hope to achieve by using repetition and short words in his poems?

_____

_____

_____

_____

Segment 3: The Writing Process
- Why does Cornelius Eady read his poems aloud as he is writing them? How can reading a poem aloud give the reader (or the writer) a different perspective of the poem?

_____

_____

_____

_____

Segment 4: The Rewards of Writing
- What does Cornelius Eady hope readers can learn from his poems? In your opinion, why might it be important to share your stories with others through writing?

_____

_____

_____

_____

Learning About Poetry

There are three main types of poetry: **Narrative** poetry tells a story and has a plot, characters, and a setting. It includes **epics,** long poems about the feats of gods or heroes, and **ballads,** songlike poems with short stanzas and a refrain. **Dramatic** poetry tells a story using a character's own thoughts or spoken statements. **Lyric** poetry expresses the feelings of a single speaker.

Poetic forms include **haiku,** poems of three unrhymed lines of five, seven, and five syllables; **tanka,** poems of five unrhymed lines of five, seven, five, seven, and seven syllables; **free verse,** which has neither a set pattern of rhythm nor rhyme; and **sonnets,** fourteen-line lyric poems with formal patterns of rhyme, rhythm, and line structure.

Poets frequently uses **figurative language** to make comparisons. **Similes** use *like* or *as* to compare unlike things; **metaphors** speak of one thing in terms of another; and **personification** gives human traits to nonhuman things.

Poets also uses **imagery** to create vivid impressions, or **images.** Images are developed using **sensory language,** which relates to the senses of sight, touch, taste, smell, hearing, and movement.

Finally, poets use **sound devices** to achieve a musical quality. They use **rhythm,** the pattern of stressed and unstressed syllables of words in sequence (an ordered pattern of rhythm is **meter**); **rhyme,** the repetition of identical or similar sounds in the last syllables of words; **alliteration,** the repetition of the initial consonant sounds of words; **assonance,** the repetition of vowel sounds in words that are close to each other; and **consonance,** the repetition of consonants in words that are close to each other and contain different vowels.

A. DIRECTIONS: *Read the description of each element of poetry. Then, write its definition. Choose from the terms in boldface type in the preceding passage.*

_____ 1. a comparison that speaks of one thing in terms of another

_____ 2. the pattern of stressed and unstressed syllables in sequence

_____ 3. a long narrative poem about the accomplishments of a hero

_____ 4. a poem without rhyme or a set pattern of rhythm

_____ 5. the repetition of similar sounds in the last syllables of words

_____ 6. nonhuman things described as having human traits

_____ 7. vivid impressions that relate to the senses

_____ 8. a fourteen-line lyric poem

B. DIRECTIONS: *Read this poem. Then, describe the form it takes and the devices it uses.*

The snow fell all night / A blanket bringing no warmth / Winter has arrived.

_____

_____

_____

_____

Name _____ Date _____

The Poetry of Cornelius Eady
Model Selection: Poetry

A lyric poem expresses the feelings of a single speaker. Lyric poems often use **figurative language,** writing that departs from the standard meaning of words to express ideas or feelings in new ways. The following are three types of figurative language.

- **similes:** comparisons that use *like* or *as* to compare two essentially unlike things
- **metaphors:** comparisons that speak of one thing in terms of another
- **personification:** comparisons that give human traits to nonhuman things

A. DIRECTIONS: *"The Poetic Interpretation of the Twist" and "The Empty Dance Shoes" are lyric poems in which the poet uses figurative language to express his feelings. Complete the following chart by writing down at least two examples of each kind of figurative language. The examples may come from either one of Eady's poems.*

Simile:
Metaphor:
Personification:

B. DIRECTIONS: *The speaker of "The Poetic Interpretation of the Twist" reveals a great deal about himself and his feelings in the poem. Describe three things you learn about the speaker, and tell how you learn each one.*

_____

_____

_____

_____

_____

Name _____ Date _____

The Poetry of Cornelius Eady
Selection Test A

Critical Thinking *Identify the letter of the choice that best answers the question.*

_____ 1. Which of the following is the best definition of a simile?
   A. an ordered pattern of rhythm
   B. a comparison using the word *like* or *as*
   C. a description that appeals to one of the five senses
   D. a comparison that gives human traits to a nonhuman thing

_____ 2. Which of the following is the best definition of meter?
   A. an ordered pattern of rhythm
   B. a songlike narrative with short stanzas
   C. the repetition of vowel sounds in nearby words
   D. a comparison that speaks of one thing in terms of another

_____ 3. Which of these terms names a sound device?
   A. epic
   B. free verse
   C. consonance
   D. metaphor

_____ 4. What sound device is most evident in the following line?
   The clack of computer keys kept crossing my mind.
   A. assonance
   B. alliteration
   C. consonance
   D. rhyme

_____ 5. Which term names a poem with five unrhymed lines of five, seven, five, seven, and seven syllables?
   A. tanka
   B. haiku
   C. sonnet
   D. ballad

Critical Reading

___ 6. What confuses the speaker in "The Poetic Interpretation of the Twist"?
   A. how the twist was done
   B. the mini-skirt and vinyl
   C. his father's actions
   D. his neighborhood

___ 7. Where did the speaker in "The Poetic Interpretation of the Twist" live?
   A. in the country, on a farm
   B. next door to a barbershop
   C. on a dead-end street
   D. in a housing project

___ 8. Why does the speaker in "The Poetic Interpretation of the Twist" mention "re-creating" his sister and his father?
   A. They are his strongest memories of the time.
   B. They died in an automobile accident.
   C. They used to do the twist together.
   D. They still live in the old neighborhood.

___ 9. Which of these lines from "The Poetic Interpretation of the Twist" contains a metaphor?
   A. "Here's a guy who must understand what the twist was all about."
   B. "Let's not forget the pool hall and the barbershop."
   C. "I must not slight the ragweed, / The true rose of the street."
   D. "My head hurts. / I am tired of remembering."

___ 10. How does the speaker's father "escape" in "The Poetic Interpretation of the Twist"?
   A. He rides his bicycle.
   B. He takes a train.
   C. He runs away at night.
   D. He dies in an accident.

___ 11. To what does the speaker in "The Empty Dance Shoes" compare the energy of dance shoes at rest?
   A. "The Colossus" by Sylvia Plath
   B. A clown knocked down by a sandbag
   C. the music in the Stardust Ballroom
   D. a 98-pound weakling

_____ 12. In "The Empty Dance Shoes," what do the empty dance shoes represent?
  A. the potential for movement
  B. death at a young age
  C. the exhaustion of old age
  D. the end of an era

_____ 13. Which of these lines from "The Empty Dance Shoes" contains a simile?
  A. "An empty pair of dance shoes / Will sit on the floor like a wart."
  B. "This is the secret of inertia: / The shoes run on their own sense of the world."
  C. "They are in sympathy with the rock the kid skips over the lake."
  D. "Hot music shakes the windows up and down the block."

_____ 14. What do the rock and the empty dance shoes have in common in "The Empty Dance Shoes"?
  A. They are both heavy.
  B. They are both skipped.
  C. They were both in motion at one time.
  D. They were both thrown into the lake by a boy.

_____ 15. Why is an empty pair of dance shoes like the answer to the question "Whose Turn Is It / To Take Out the Garbage"?
  A. Both require a change.
  B. Both lead to exhaustion.
  C. Neither can be understood.
  D. Neither involves movement.

Essay

16. The subject of "The Poetic Interpretation of the Twist" is the twist, a dance that was popular in the 1960s. In an essay, describe the kinds of things the speaker thinks about when he tries to explain "what the twist was all about." Mention three details from the poem in your response.

17. The speaker in "The Empty Dance Shoes" compares the shoes to various things, including a wart, a pressed leaf, and a rock that a boy has skipped over a lake. In an essay, discuss the comparisons. How are the things that the shoes are compared to similar to the shoes? What is the effect of the comparisons—what do they say about the empty dance shoes?

Name _____ Date _____

The Poetry of Cornelius Eady
Selection Test B

Critical Thinking *Identify the letter of the choice that best completes the statement or answers the question.*

____ 1. What kind of figurative language is used in these lines?

   The skies shared our sorrow / And wept a cold rain.

   A. metaphor
   B. personification
   C. simile using *like*
   D. simile using *as*

____ 2. Imagery is created through the use of
   A. rhythm and rhyme.
   B. sensory language.
   C. narration.
   D. sound devices.

____ 3. Which of the following terms name a sound device?
   I.   imagery
   II. assonance
   III. consonance
   IV. alliteration
   A. I, II, and III
   B. II, III, and IV
   C. I, II, and IV
   D. I, III, and IV

____ 4. Which of the following is the best definition of an epic poem?
   A. a poem that tells a story using a character's thoughts
   B. a long narrative poem about gods or heroes
   C. a songlike narrative with stanzas and a refrain
   D. a poem that expresses the feelings of a single speaker

____ 5. A lyric poem
   A. often tells about a real person.
   B. always has a regular rhythm.
   C. never includes metaphors.
   D. expresses a speaker's feelings.

____ 6. Poems in free verse are characterized by
   A. no rhyme or set pattern of rhythm.
   B. three lines of five, seven, and five syllables.
   C. fourteen lines with formal patterns of rhyme and rhythm.
   D. five lines of five, seven, five, seven, and seven syllables.

Critical Reading

____ 7. To whom is the speaker in "The Poetic Interpretation of the Twist" speaking?
A. to the reader
B. to himself
C. to his sister
D. to his father

____ 8. What does the speaker in "The Poetic Interpretation of the Twist" mean when he says, "I am still confused by the mini-skirt"?
A. He does not understand why fashions changed in the 1960s.
B. He does not understand the changes brought by the 1960s.
C. He does not understand why women wore mini-skirts.
D. He does not understand why his sister wore mini-skirts.

____ 9. To the speaker in "The Poetic Interpretation of the Twist," the twist was
A. a sign of the times.
B. the foundation of a bridge.
C. a troublesome responsibility.
D. a children's game.

____ 10. The speaker in "The Poetic Interpretation of the Twist" compares his sister to a giraffe to show that
A. she has orange hair.
B. she is awkward.
C. she is fast.
D. she loves animals.

____ 11. What kind of figurative language do these lines from "The Poetic Interpretation of the Twist" express?

    The twist is . . . / . . . the foundation of a bridge / That has made way for a housing project.

A. a simile using *like*
B. personification
C. a metaphor
D. a simile using *as*

____ 12. How does the speaker in "The Poetic Interpretation of the Twist" remember the twist?
A. He does not remember it at all.
B. He remembers it with perfect clarity.
C. He remembers it the way a baby remembers meeting a distant relative.
D. He remembers it as well as he remembers his old neighborhood and his family.

____ 13. What is the "entire world" that the speaker in "The Poetic Interpretation of the Twist" has on the tip of his tongue?
A. all his memories
B. the world of dance
C. his school years
D. his family

____ 14. "The Poetic Interpretation of the Twist" is a lyric poem because
A. it does not have a set pattern of rhyme.
B. it expresses a single speaker's feelings.
C. it uses figurative language.
D. it tells a story and has a plot.

____ 15. According to "The Empty Dance Shoes," how is an empty pair of dancing shoes like a pressed leaf?
A. Both were once in motion.
B. Both were once part of nature.
C. Both used to be alive.
D. Neither moves in wintertime.

____ 16. In "The Empty Dance Shoes," what happens to the shoes "in the middle of the Stardust Ballroom"?
A. They take on the energy of the room.
B. They are exhausted by the excitement.
C. They find a reason to move.
D. They remain the same as before.

____ 17. What kind of figurative language does this line from "The Empty Dance Shoes" contain?
An empty pair of dance shoes / Is a lot like the answer to this question.

A. a metaphor
B. a simile using *like*
C. personification
D. a simile using *as*

____ 18. The speaker in "The Empty Dance Shoes" compares the energy in an empty pair of dancing shoes to
A. a book by Sylvia Plath.
B. the ripples of a rock skipped on water.
C. a wart, a clown, a leaf, and a rock.
D. scientists who study inertia.

____ 19. What is the "different set of scientific principles" that the 98-pound weakling acts on at the end of "The Empty Dance Shoes"?
A. the impulse to move
B. the rules of gravity
C. the power of love
D. the theory of relativity

____ 20. What type of poem is "The Empty Dance Shoes"?
A. a ballad
B. a narrative poem
C. a lyric poem
D. a tanka

Essay

21. Sir Isaac Newton's law of inertia states in part that "a body at rest will remain at rest." In an essay, tell how the end of "The Empty Dance Shoes" defies that law. Use at least two details from the poem to support your response.

22. In "The Poetic Interpretation of the Twist," the speaker compares the twist to the "foundation of a bridge / That has made way for a housing project." In an essay, explain what the speaker is saying about the twist in those lines.

23. What question is the speaker in "The Poetic Interpretation of the Twist" answering? In an essay, discuss that question. What expectation does the question raise, and why does the speaker find it "a troublesome responsibility"?

Name _____

Unit 4: Poetry
Part 1 Concept Map

Reading Skills and Strategies: Reading Fluently

To appreciate and share the musical qualities of Poetry

Academic Vocabulary words you can use to discuss reading fluently

you can

read aloud and adjust your reading rate

and by

previewing the work

(demonstrated in this selection)

Selection name:

Literary Analysis: Poetry

Poems

have

a speaker

and follow

a poetic form

(demonstrated in this selection)

Selection name:

(demonstrated in this selection)

Selection name:

Reading Informational Materials: Research Sources

You can locate information in research sources

by

previewing the text, and by skimming, and scanning

Characteristics of Poetry
- Figurative language
- Figures of Speech
- Imagery
- Rhythm
- Rhyme
- Alliteration

Types of Poetry
- Narrative
- Dramatic
- Lyric

Forms of Poetry
- haiku
- tanka
- free verse
- sonnet

Comparing Literary Works: Tone and Mood

create the overall feeling of a literary work by

a writer's choice of subject and setting **(mood)**

a writer's choice of words, descriptive details, and images **(tone)**

(demonstrated in these selections)

Selection names:
1.
2.

Part 1 Student Log

Complete this chart to track your assignments.

Writing	Extend Your Learning	Writing Workshop	Other Assignments

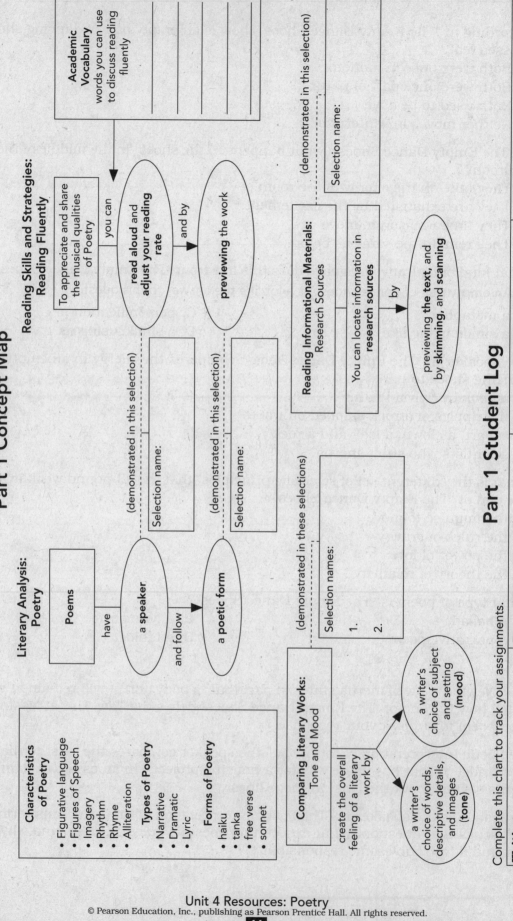

Unit 4: Poetry
Part 1 Diagnostic Test 7

MULTIPLE CHOICE

Read the selection. Then, answer the questions that follow.

One day a fox boasted to a cat about how clever he was, saying, "My bag of tricks is so ample that I can escape my enemies, the dogs, in over a hundred different ways."

"Oh really? How awfully clever!" replied the cat. "I have a single trick," she added, "but it nearly always works."

"That may be all very well," the fox retorted, "but you must scarcely doubt that, of all the animals in the forest, I am surely the cleverest."

"You are indeed remarkable," purred the cat.

"Sometime I must teach you one or two of my easier tricks," said the fox.

Just then they heard the baying of a pack of hounds, coming toward the exact spot where the cat and the fox were conversing, and immediately, the cat raced up a tree and disappeared in the foliage.

"That's my one and only trick," she called down to the fox. "What trick are you going to use?"

But the fox was paralyzed by indecision, and he couldn't decide which trick to use. The dogs, meanwhile, came nearer and nearer. Too late, the fox broke into a run, and the dogs had no difficulty catching him—and that was the end of the fox, and of his bag of tricks.

1. Who is the main character in this fable?
   A. the cat
   B. the fox
   C. a hound
   D. a dog

2. What is the subject of the fox's boasting?
   A. his many ways of escaping the dogs
   B. his ability to plan ahead
   C. how much cleverer he is than cats
   D. how much cleverer he is than dogs

3. Which of the following best describes how the cat responds to the fox's boasting?
   A. She tells the fox that she has only one trick.
   B. She warns the fox not to boast.
   C. She warns the fox that the dogs are coming.
   D. She calls the dogs to chase the fox.

4. How does the cat react when the hounds begin baying?
   A. The cat hides in the bushes.
   B. The cat begins snarling.
   C. The cat hisses at the hounds.
   D. The cat races up the tree.

5. What is the cat's one and only trick?
   A. hissing at the dogs
   B. scratching and clawing
   C. running up a tree
   D. running away

6. Which of the following best describes how the fox reacts to the baying of the hounds?
   A. The fox freezes in indecision.
   B. The fox runs away.
   C. The fox tries to follow the cat.
   D. The fox begins baying as well.

7. What happens to the fox in the end?
   A. He becomes fast friends with the cat.
   B. He boasts how he escapes the dogs.
   C. He becomes friends with the hounds.
   D. He tries to run, but the dogs catch him.

8. Which of the following best states the moral of this fable?
   A. When faced with danger, a person should always be decisive.
   B. A single plan that works is better than a hundred doubtful alternatives.
   C. A person should have many plans for escaping danger.
   D. A clever person has just one plan for escaping danger.

Read the selection. Then, answer the questions that follow.

An eagle and a fox had been amicable neighbors for a long time, each respecting the other. The eagle had built a nest at the top of a high tree, where she was rearing eaglets. At the foot of that same tree, deep in a hole, lived the fox, who had one cub.

One day the eagle, forgetting friendship, eyed the fox cub from her perch aloft in the tree, and while the mother fox was away, she pounced on the cub, carrying it away for her babies.

When the mother fox returned and realized the betrayal of trust she bitterly upbraided the eagle.

"Is this how friends should behave?" she burst out reproachfully.

The fox pleaded and pleaded, but the mother eagle ignored the fox's piteous entreaties, and she prepared to feed the cub to her babies.

Desperate, the mother fox rushed to a place where she knew a fire would be burning at a shrine in the forest, and quickly she snatched a burning branch and ran back to the tree. Now it was the mother eagle's turn to fear: her babies were ravenous, but what if the fox set fire to the tree?

"Hold on!" the eagle finally screamed, "I'll bring your cub back to you at once!"

9. What is the relationship between the eagle and the fox?
   A. They are fierce enemies.
   B. They are friendly neighbors.
   C. They are close friends.
   D. They are bitter competitors.

10. In what task are the fox and the eagle engaged as the fable opens?
    A. pursuing food
    B. building nests
    C. digging a hole
    D. raising babies

11. Why does the eagle steal the fox's baby?
    A. to feed to her babies
    B. to get even with the fox
    C. to force the fox to move
    D. as a playmate for her babies

12. How does the fox react to the eagle's actions?
    A. The fox burns down the tree containing the eagle's nest.
    B. The fox steals the eagle's babies.
    C. The fox pleads for the return of her baby.
    D. The fox tries to harm the eagle.

13. How does the fox force the eagle to return her baby?

    A. The fox tries to steal the eagle babies from their nest.

    B. The fox threatens to set the tree on fire and burn the eagle babies.

    C. The fox threatens to enlist the aid of hunters to kill the eagle.

    D. The fox offers to bring other food to feed the eagle babies.

14. What decision must the eagle mother make in the end?

    A. to return the fox's baby or to remain enemies with the fox

    B. to keep the fox's baby or find other food for her babies

    C. to lose her babies to fire or face the possibility of their starvation

    D. to risk having fire destroy her nest or to move to a new nest

15. Which of the following is the best statement of the moral of this fable?

    A. Be careful about whom you choose for your neighbors.

    B. Do not harm others if you do not wish them to harm you.

    C. Make sure you always keep your children well fed.

    D. Do not be too quick to trust those who claim to be your friend.

Vocabulary Warm-up Word Lists

Study these words from the poetry of Pushkin, García Lorca, Bishop, and Kipling. Then, apply your knowledge to the activities that follow.

Word List A

battered [BAT uhrd] *adj.* beaten; injured
Our cat came home looking <u>battered</u> after fighting with a stray.

fast [FAST] *adj.* firm; fixed
The father held his young daughter's hand <u>fast</u> as they boarded the train.

headlong [HED lawng] *adj.* with uncontrolled speed; head first
The unsaddled horse ran <u>headlong</u> into the meadow.

mourns [MAWRNZ] *v.* feels sorrow for; grieves for something dead
My aunt still <u>mourns</u> for her husband who died many years ago.

seize [SEEZ] *v.* to take quickly; to grab
To capture a runaway cat, never <u>seize</u> it by the tail.

whimpers [WIM puhrz] *v.* cries softly
The dog <u>whimpers</u> quietly and begs for food with big, sad eyes.

Word List B

distraught [dis TRAWT] *adj.* very troubled
I felt nervous and <u>distraught</u> after losing my backpack at the library.

infested [in FES tid] *adj.* overrun by something
An old house might be <u>infested</u> with mice.

regiment [REJ uh muhnt] *n.* a military unit of two or more battalions
There was a parade when my sister's army <u>regiment</u> returned from the war.

tarnished [TAHR nisht] *adj.* dulled; stained
Our silverware is <u>tarnished</u> because we never polish it.

tumult [TOO mult] *n.* noisy confusion
The game was little more than a <u>tumult</u> because no one followed the rules.

vaults [VAWLTZ] *n.* arched spaces; the arches of the sky
The cloudless sky was brilliant against the <u>vaults</u> of the treetops.

Poetry Collection: Alexander Pushkin, Federico García Lorca,
Elizabeth Bishop, Rudyard Kipling
Vocabulary Warm-up Exercises

Exercise A *Fill in each blank in the paragraph with an appropriate word from Word List A.
Use each word only once.*

As Paula's parents kiss her goodbye, she flings herself onto the floor, holding

[1] _____ to her father's ankle. She [2] _____ like a

wounded kitten, but her parents know she is acting. They [3] _____ her

hands and tickle her until she lets go. As soon as the door closes behind them, Paula

runs [4] _____ into her parent's bedroom. She flings herself onto their

bed and kicks at the [5] _____ headboard, which has witnessed many

similar scenes. As Paula [6] _____ her parents' departure, her sitter gets

an idea. She shows Paula a lipstick on her mother's dressing table. Soon, Paula's lips

and face are covered with pink lipstick, and Paula is finally ready to enjoy the evening.

Exercise B *Decide whether each statement is true or false. Circle* T *or* F. *Then, explain your
answer.*

1. If a house is <u>infested</u> with termites, fewer people will want to buy it.
   T / F _____

2. It is easy to sleep during a lot of <u>tumult</u>.
   T / F _____

3. Dull silver can be polished, but a <u>tarnished</u> reputation can never be improved.
   T / F _____

4. Feeding a <u>regiment</u> would require a huge kitchen and a lot of food.
   T / F _____

5. The <u>vaults</u> of the sky usually darken during a storm.
   T / F _____

6. Most people would feel <u>distraught</u> if they woke up on another planet.
   T / F _____

Name _____ Date _____

Poetry Collection: Alexander Pushkin, Federico García Lorca, Elizabeth Bishop, Rudyard Kipling

Reading Warm-up A

Read the following passage. Pay special attention to the underlined words. Then, read it again, and complete the activities. Use a separate sheet of paper for your written answers.

Outside our tent, Razzo rubs his nose into the ground and it comes up speckled with dirt. I guess that is what you get when you take a dog camping.

Suddenly, something <u>whimpers</u> in the distance, a soft cry that sounds shy and afraid. Razzo runs full-speed into the bushes toward the unknown noise.

We both stop short when we see the raccoon. Its hind leg is caught in a metal grill that another camper must have carelessly left behind. The grill is totally <u>battered</u>, bent in several places and very rusty. The raccoon has been trying to get free, but its leg is held <u>fast</u> by the bent metal.

My first impulse is to <u>seize</u> the grill and pull it off, but I know that grabbing the metal could be dangerous. A scared, wild animal might scratch or bite me, even if I am trying to help.

Razzo starts barking, which is not making things any easier, so I bring him back to the tent. I tie him up and head back to the raccoon with two long branches. I hold down the grill with one branch and carefully bend the bars with the other. At first, they do not budge, but finally the bars begin to spread apart. In an instant, the foot slips through and the raccoon makes a <u>headlong</u> dash into the woods.

Back at the tent, Razzo looks very upset. I know that he <u>mourns</u> the lost raccoon, wishing that he could have played with the strange new animal. We both need to calm down a little, so I take out my guitar and play Razzo's favorite song, a slow waltz. As soon as the music starts, he curls up at my side. Maybe the guitar's sweet song will bring a dream of running and playing with his new friend, the raccoon.

1. Underline the words that describe how something <u>whimpers</u>. Then, tell what *whimpers* means.

2. Underline the words that describe how the <u>battered</u> grill looked. Then, explain what *battered* means.

3. Underline the words that explain what is held <u>fast</u> by the grill. Then, explain why *fast* does not mean "quick" in this sentence.

4. Circle what the narrator might <u>seize</u>. Then, tell why it would not be a good idea to *seize* a wild animal.

5. Describe how someone looks who is making a *headlong* dash.

6. Circle the words that tell what the dog <u>mourns</u>. Then, explain how someone who *mourns* might act.

Poetry Collection: Alexander Pushkin, Federico García Lorca,
Elizabeth Bishop, Rudyard Kipling

Reading Warm-up B

Read the following passage. Pay special attention to the underlined words. Then, read it again, and complete the activities. Use a separate sheet of paper for your written answers.

The spirit of an army is called *morale*. Military leaders have long recognized the importance of promoting high, positive morale in their troops. In wartime, high morale can mean the difference between success and defeat.

Soldiers must be able to handle the <u>tumult</u> of war, with its extreme noise and confusion. Troops with low morale could easily become <u>distraught</u> due to the difficult conditions they experience. Combat is never steady. Short periods of action alternate with longer periods of waiting. Effective leaders know that soldiers must also learn to handle these difficult slow periods. Soldiers often live far from the familiar comforts of home. Their forks might be <u>tarnished</u> and old, their clothing filthy. Their living quarters might be <u>infested</u> with fleas, lice, or other bugs.

Leaders use a variety of strategies to boost morale under these harsh conditions. Many United States services have a Department of Morale, Welfare, and Recreation. These departments offer services designed to help soldiers relax. They provide everything from entertainment to reading material to exercise equipment. For example, all of the soldiers in one <u>regiment</u> might participate in an ongoing game, such as creating an imaginary baseball league.

Napoleon said, "Morale is to the physical as three is to one," suggesting that an army with high morale is three times stronger than one without it. Troops sleeping in tents under the <u>vaults</u> of a foreign sky will become homesick. An effective leader finds ways to remind them that the same sky also extends over the homes for which they yearn.

1. Circle the words that describe the <u>tumult</u> of war. Then, describe a time when you were in the middle of a *tumult*.

2. Underline the words that tell why troops might be <u>distraught</u>. Then, tell what *distraught* means.

3. Circle the word that names something that can be <u>tarnished</u>. Then, write a sentence about something else that can be *tarnished*.

4. Circle three words naming things with which areas might become <u>infested</u>. Then, tell what *infested* means.

5. Circle the word that names the kind of people in a <u>regiment</u>. Then, tell where you might find a *regiment*.

6. Underline the words that describe the <u>vaults</u> under which tents stand. Then, tell what *vaults* means.

Name _____ Date _____

Poetry Collection: Alexander Pushkin, Federico García Lorca, Elizabeth Bishop,
and Rudyard Kipling

Literary Analysis: Narrative and Lyric Poetry

In poetry, the **speaker** is the voice that says the words of the poem. All poems have a speaker, who is either the poet or a character the poet invents to give the poem a particular voice or point of view.

- In **narrative** poetry, the speaker tells a story in verse.
- In **lyric poetry,** the speaker's thoughts, feelings, and insights create a single, unified impression. Lyric poems include **imagery,** language that appeals to the senses.

DIRECTIONS: *Answer the following questions about the poems in this collection.*

1. "The Bridegroom" begins with these lines:

   For three days Natasha, / The merchant's daughter, / Was missing. The third night, / She ran in, distraught.

   Based on these lines, is "The Bridegroom" a narrative poem or a lyric poem? Explain.

   _____

   _____

2. Identify two examples of imagery in the following lines from "The Guitar." Tell which senses the images appeal to and what feeling the lines create.

   It weeps / For distant things, / Warm southern sands / Desiring white camellias.

   _____

   _____

   _____

3. When the speaker of "The Fish" examines the fish she has caught, she sees five old pieces of fishing line in its jaw, signs that the fish has been hooked before, but got away:

   Like medals with their ribbons / frayed and wavering, / a five-haired beard of wisdom / trailing from his aching jaw.

   What does the speaker's imagery tell you about her feelings toward the fish?

   _____

   _____

4. Read lines 3–6 of "Danny Deever," and then explain how Kipling uses dialogue to tell a story in this poem?

   _____

   _____

   _____

Poetry Collection: Alexander Pushkin, Federico García Lorca, Elizabeth Bishop, and Rudyard Kipling

Reading: Read Aloud and Adjust Reading Rate to Read Fluently

Read aloud to appreciate and share the musical qualities of poetry. As you read aloud, **read fluently** and **adjust your reading rate** in the following ways.

- First, read through slowly and carefully. Make sure you understand the poem's complex thoughts and that you can pronounce all the words.
- Use punctuation and group words for meaning. Do not pause at the end of a line unless a punctuation mark indicates that you should.
- Slow down to emphasize an idea or the sounds of words.

The following chart shows how to mark up a poem to help you read it fluently:

Mark the Text	Adjusting Reading Rate
Circle punctuation marks.	Pause.
Underline words or sounds to emphasize.	Slow down.
Bracket phrases or groups of words to read together.	Speed up.

DIRECTIONS: *Write your answers to the following questions.*

1. Copy lines 61–64 of "The Bridegroom" onto a separate sheet of paper and circle all the punctuation marks. Then, answer the questions.

   A. How many complete sentences do the lines contain? _____

   B. After which words should readers pause briefly?

   _____

2. Line 25 of "The Guitar" ends with an exclamation point—"O guitar!" How does this punctuation mark affect the reading of the line?

   _____

   _____

3. Copy lines 7–11 of "The Fish" onto a separate sheet of paper. Then, follow the directions below.

   A. Underline the three adjectives that a reader should emphasize when reading the poem aloud.

   B. Bracket each group of words a reader should say together to make the meaning of the phrase that begins "Here and there . . ." clear.

4. Read aloud the opening lines of "Danny Deever." Then explain the importance that quotation marks and question marks play in reading the poem fluently.

   _____

   _____

   _____

Name _____ Date _____

Poetry Collection: Alexander Pushkin, Federico García Lorca, Elizabeth Bishop, and Rudyard Kipling

Vocabulary Builder

Word List

foreboding	monotonously	recruits	venerable

A. DIRECTIONS: *In each item below, think about the meaning of the italicized word and then answer the question.*

1. When might you have a feeling of *foreboding* about taking a test?

   _____

2. How would you feel if a speaker talked *monotonously* about his subject?

   _____

3. How would you treat a *venerable* visitor?

   _____

4. How does the army get *recruits*?

   _____

B. DIRECTIONS: *Circle the letter of the word that best completes each sentence.*

1. The *venerable* leader was generally _____.
   A. hated
   B. admired
   C. ignored
   D. mocked

2. A new group of *recruits* always lacks _____.
   A. intelligence
   B. talent
   C. experience
   D. parents

3. I felt such a sense of *foreboding* that I _____.
   A. smiled
   B. relaxed
   C. celebrated
   D. trembled

Name _____ Date _____

Support for Writing a Lyric Poem

After you choose a speaker and a subject for your lyric poem, use the following graphic organizer to list imagery that describes the subject.

Subject being described: _____

Speaker in poem: _____

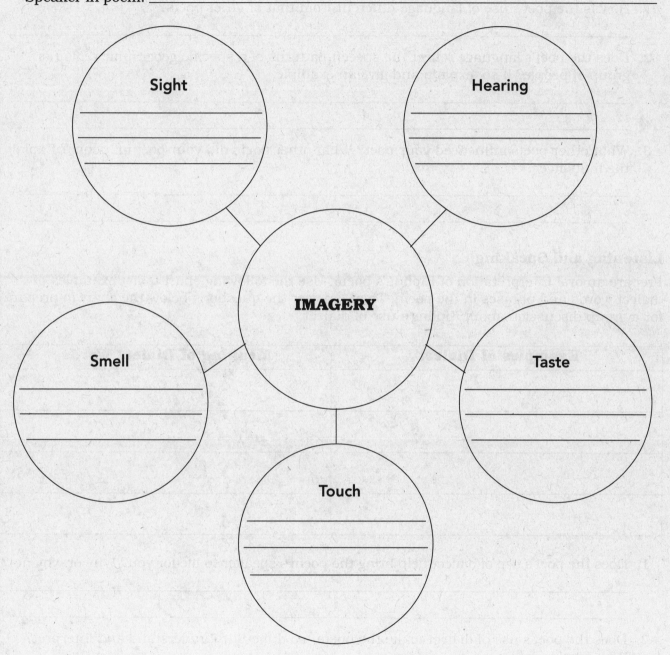

Now, use your notes to write a lyric poem that vividly describes the subject and conveys the speaker's feelings about it.

Poetry Collection: Alexander Pushkin, Federico García Lorca, Elizabeth Bishop, and Rudyard Kipling

Support for Extend Your Learning

Research and Technology

Use the lines below to gather information for a research report. Choose one poet from this group. Find information that answers the following questions about the poet's use of language.

1. How is the poet's use of language different from that of other poets?

   _____

2. Does the poet's language reflect the speech patterns of a specific geographic region or group of people? If so, explain and give an example.

   _____

   _____

3. What other poets influenced your poet? What other poets did your poet influence? Explain the influences.

   _____

   _____

Listening and Speaking

Prepare an oral interpretation of Kipling's poem. Use the following chart to list examples of dialect words and phrases in the poem. Then, answer the questions below the chart to prepare for a group discussion about Kipling's use of dialect.

Examples of Dialect	Meaning of Dialect Words

1. Does the poet's use of dialect help bring the poem's speaker to life for you? Why or why not?

   _____

   _____

2. Does the poet's use of dialect make the poem too difficult to understand and interpret? Why or why not?

   _____

   _____

Poetry Collection: Alexander Pushkin, Federico García Lorca, Elizabeth Bishop,
and Rudyard Kipling

Enrichment: Random Acts of Kindness

Some readers might call the speaker's action in "The Fish" a random act of kindness. The speaker could have kept the fish as a trophy—or as a meal. Instead, she is overcome by wonder at the fish's spirit of endurance, by its stubborn persistence in the struggle for life, and she decides to let it go. Her act qualifies as a random act of kindness for the following reasons:

- The act is clearly an act of giving, beneficial to another creature.
- The act is a direct, thoughtful response to immediate circumstances. It is not the result of habit or planning.
- The motive for the act is the speaker's own delight in doing it. No one is pleading with her to do it. There are no onlookers to impress.

Most of us have opportunities every day to perform random acts of kindness. Consider these examples:

- An empty-handed shopper offers to help a senior citizen across an icy section of sidewalk.
- Marie knows that her neighbor Jackie has been home with two sick children for two days and that Jackie's husband is away on business. Marie calls Jackie to ask if there is anything she can pick up for her when she goes to the store.
- Joe's mom has an important presentation to make at work today. If she impresses her boss, she may get a promotion. Joe has dinner waiting for her when she gets home, ready to celebrate or console as the outcome of the presentation warrants.

DIRECTIONS: *During the next week, perform two random acts of kindness. Make sure that your acts are not just simple courtesies. Use this table to record your acts, as well as the reaction of the recipient of each act and your own feelings about each act. Consider sharing your experiences in a class discussion.*

	Random Act of Kindness 1	Random Act of Kindness 2
Act		
How the recipient responded		
How the act made me feel		

Poetry Collection: Alexander Pushkin, Federico García Lorca, Elizabeth Bishop, and Rudyard Kipling

Selection Test A

Critical Reading *Identify the letter of the choice that best answers the question.*

____ 1. Why is "The Bridegroom" considered a narrative poem?
   A. because it has a speaker
   B. because it tells a story
   C. because it creates a single impression
   D. because it is so long

____ 2. What happens at the very beginning of "The Bridegroom"?
   A. Natasha tells about a scary dream.
   B. Natasha sees a man and screams.
   C. Natasha returns after being missing.
   D. Natasha has the police arrest someone.

____ 3. By the end of the poem, what can you guess about Natasha and the bridegroom?
   A. Natasha saw the bridegroom murder another girl.
   B. Natasha is mistaken in her fear of the bridegroom.
   C. The bridegroom will help Natasha recover from her scary dream.
   D. The bridegroom is already married to someone else.

____ 4. Why is "The Guitar" considered a lyric poem?
   A. because it has a speaker
   B. because it tells a story
   C. because it creates a single impression
   D. because it is so short

____ 5. Where should a reader pause when reading aloud the following lines from "The Guitar"?
   > Now begins the cry
   > Of the guitar,
   > Breaking the vaults
   > Of dawn. [p. 973, ll 1–4]

   A. Do not pause after any line.
   B. Pause briefly after each line.
   C. Pause after lines 1 and 3.
   D. Pause after lines 2 and 4.

____ 6. What feeling is conveyed by the imagery in "The Guitar"?

    A. joy

    B. sadness

    C. surprise

    D. anger

____ 7. Which sentence summarizes the story told in "The Fish"?

    A. A woman catches a fish but the fish gets away.

    B. A woman catches a fish and takes it home for dinner.

    C. A woman catches a fish and then lets it go.

    D. A woman catches a fish that grants her three wishes.

____ 8. How many complete sentences would be said in reading aloud the following lines from "The Fish"?

    He hung a grunting weight,
    battered and and venerable
    and homely. [p. 293, ll. 7–9]

    A. none

    B. one

    C. two

    D. three

____ 9. To which of the five senses does the following imagery from "The Fish" appeal?

    He was speckled with barnacles,
    fine rosettes of lime, [p. 293, ll. 16–17]

    A. sight

    B. hearing

    C. taste

    D. touch

____ 10. What event is described in the poem "Danny Deever"?

    A. a military battle

    B. a military parade

    C. a military inspection

    D. a military execution

____ 11. In "Danny Deever," why is Files-on-Parade upset?

    A. He feels sad because a man he knows is about to be killed.

    B. He feels afraid because he is going into his first battle.

    C. He feels guilty for lying to the Color-Sergeant.

    D. He feels ashamed of his ignorance of military justice.

___ **12.** How are the poems "The Bridegroom" and "Danny Deever" alike?

    A. They are both set in England in the 1800s.

    B. They both describe military life.

    C. The both describe the dangers of romantic love.

    D. They both use dialogue to tell a dramatic story.

Vocabulary and Grammar

___ **13.** In "The Bridegroom," why are Natasha's parents "Stricken with *foreboding*"?

    A. because they are excited about planning Natasha's wedding

    B. because they are afraid something bad will happen to Natasha

    C. because they are angry that Natasha has been misbehaving

    D. because they feel guilty after Natasha gets hurt badly

___ **14.** Which item below is an object used mainly for *visual* purposes?

    A. a microscope

    B. a telephone

    C. a bottle of perfume

    D. a soft scarf

___ **15.** Which sentence does NOT include a prepositional phrase?

    A. I went to the store for some eggs.

    B. The letter from Hank was funny.

    C. I went swimming yesterday morning.

    D. The woman on the right is Sarah.

Essay

16. Choose one of the narrative poems in this group and write a brief essay that summarizes the story it tells. Describe the main characters and the setting. Discuss two or three important events.

17. Which of the four poems seems to express the strongest feelings? In a brief essay, describe the feeling the poem conveys. Then, explain how the poet uses vivid descriptions or a dramatic story to create this feeling.

Poetry Collection: Alexander Pushkin, Federico García Lorca, Elizabeth Bishop, and Rudyard Kipling

Selection Test B

Critical Reading *Identify the letter of the choice that best answers the question.*

____ 1. Why is "The Bridegroom" considered a narrative poem?
   A. It has strong visual imagery.
   B. It has characters and a plot.
   C. It is more than a hundred lines long.
   D. It has no specific speaker.

____ 2. In "The Bridegroom," what is the dream that Natasha describes?
   A. a vision she had when the bridegroom drove by
   B. the nightmare she had every night while she was missing
   C. an eyewitness account of the murder she witnessed
   D. a story the police asked her to tell to trap a murderer

____ 3. From the beginning of "The Bridegroom" to the end, how does Natasha change?
   A. from a frightened girl to a strong woman
   B. from a shy daughter to a bitter fiancée
   C. from a lazy dreamer to a practical wife
   D. from a mischievous child to a criminal

____ 4. When reading "The Bridegroom" aloud, why is the punctuation of these lines important?
   The groom blanches, / Trembles. Confusion . . . / Seize him! the law commands.

   A. The pauses give listeners time to understand what is going on.
   B. The pauses give the reader time to take a breath.
   C. The pauses indicate that the bridegroom has escaped.
   D. The pauses build suspense for the narrative's climax.

____ 5. To what is "The Guitar" compared?
   A. a singer
   B. camellias
   C. a wounded heart
   D. snowfall

____ 6. Which phrase best describes "The Guitar"?
   A. a lyric poem with a sad, mournful mood
   B. a lyric poem that conveys the playfulness of strumming
   C. a narrative poem about a man who loves great music
   D. a narrative poem about how a love song was written

____ 7. Why does the speaker of "The Guitar" love the instrument?
   A. It provides entertainment.
   B. It expresses human longing.
   C. It makes people get up and dance.
   D. It conveys the history of music.

____ 8. Which phrase best describes "The Fish"?
    A. a lyric poem that conveys a sad, mournful mood
    B. a lyric poem that conveys the peaceful pleasures of fishing
    C. a lyric poem with narrative elements of conflict and suspense
    D. a lyric poem with several characters struggling against nature

____ 9. To which senses does the following imagery from "The Fish" appeal?
    and a fine black thread / still crimped from the strain and snap

    A. sight, touch, hearing
    B. sight, hearing, taste
    C. hearing, touch, smell
    D. hearing, taste, sight

____ 10. When the speaker of "The Fish" studies the fish's jaw, what does she realize?
    A. The fish has been sick for a long time.
    B. The fish escaped capture five times.
    C. The fish is too small to hold onto.
    D. The fish is a rare, valuable species.

____ 11. In "The Fish," how can the speaker's attitude toward the fish best be described?
    A. angry and vengeful
    B. amazed and skeptical
    C. admiring and compassionate
    D. amused and condescending

____ 12. Which two words should a reader emphasize in these lines from "The Fish"?
    Like medals with the ribbons / frayed and wavering / a five-haired beard of wisdom

    A. medals, ribbons
    B. frayed, wavering
    C. five, beard
    D. medals, wisdom

____ 13. Which of the following elements makes "Danny Deever" difficult to read aloud?
    A. The speakers talk in a specific kind of dialect.
    B. The poet does not identify which speaker is talking.
    C. Each man speaks the exact same number of lines.
    D. The reader does not know what is going on until the end.

____ 14. In "Danny Deever," what do File-on-Parade's questions reveal about him?
    A. Files-on-Parade is less experienced than the Color-Sergeant.
    B. Files-on-Parade is less sympathetic than the Color-Sergeant.
    C. Files-on-Parade is more frustrated than the Color-Sergeant.
    D. Files-on-Parade is more ashamed than the Color-Sergeant.

____ 15. In "Danny Deever," why is Files-on-Parade especially disturbed by the execution?
    A. He actually committed the crime.
    B. He informed on Danny Deever.
    C. Danny Deever is someone he knows.
    D. Danny Deever begged him for mercy.

Vocabulary and Grammar

____ 16. What does the speaker of "The Fish" mean when she describes the fish as *venerable*?
A. The fish is ugly and repulsive.
B. The fish is worthy of respect.
C. The fish is inexperienced.
D. The fish is wild and fierce.

____ 17. If you read a poem *monotonously,* how will your audience likely react?
A. with cheers of approval
B. with gasps of fright
C. with chuckles of delight
D. with yawns of boredom

____ 18. Which sentence uses a vocabulary word INCORRECTLY?
A. The visual impact of the huge movie screen is awe-inspiring.
B. Eating lunch ten minutes later than usual is a radical change.
C. People with diverse opinions can have an interesting debate.
D. With hard work, people often compensate for weaknesses.

____ 19. In the following sentence, which word is the object of the preposition *to*?
There was a sticker glued to the back of the picture frame.
A. sticker
B. back
C. picture
D. frame

Essay

20. The poems in this group explore powerful themes about music, evil, compassion, and death. In an essay, discuss how the theme, or message about life, is conveyed in one of the poems. Explain how the poet uses imagery or a dramatic narrative to convey the theme.

21. The four poems in this group include examples of both lyric poetry and narrative poetry. Based on your responses to these poems, which type of poetry do you enjoy more? In a brief essay, identify one lyric poem and one narrative poem from the group. Summarize the main impression or the story conveyed in each poem. Then, describe your response to each poem and tell which lyric or narrative elements you especially enjoyed in the poem you prefer.

22. In both "The Fish" and "The Bridegroom," someone experiences conflict and then finally makes a decision that resolves the suspense in the poem and determines the poem's theme. In a brief essay, compare and contrast the decisions in these two poems. Describe who makes each decision, what conflict the person experiences in making the choice, and what motivates the final choice. Then, describe how each poet creates suspense until the moment of the decision. Finally, compare and contrast the message, or insight, conveyed by each decision.

Vocabulary Warm-up Word Lists

Study these words from the poetry of Levertov, Williams, Frost, and Nye. Then, apply your knowledge to the activities that follow.

Word List A

burden [BER dn] *n.* a heavy load
> The exhausted mule struggled under the weight of its <u>burden</u>.

confidence [KAHN fi duhns] *n.* belief in one's own abilities
> She showed <u>confidence</u> as she presented her science project to the judges.

dignity [DIG ni tee] *n.* honor; being worthy of respect
> Despite his humble job, the street sweeper carried himself with great <u>dignity</u>.

moisten [MOYS in] *v.* to make wet
> He sprinkled just enough water on the plant to <u>moisten</u> the soil.

sluggish [SLUG ish] *adj.* slow; lacking in energy
> The tropical heat made us so <u>sluggish</u> that we preferred resting to swimming.

unanswerable [un AN suhr uh buhl] *adj.* not able to be answered
> Her question was so poorly worded that it was actually <u>unanswerable</u>.

Word List B

clarity [KLAIR i tee] *n.* clearness; state of being clearly expressed
> If a speech is presented with <u>clarity</u>, the audience will understand it.

contagious [kuhn TAY juhs] *adj.* spreading from person to person
> Her laughter was so <u>contagious</u> that we were all soon laughing along.

earnest [ER nist] *adj.* sincere; serious
> My brother is so <u>earnest</u> that he never makes sarcastic jokes.

outermost [OW tuhr mohst] *adj.* farthest out
> The center of the rug is in good shape, but the <u>outermost</u> edges are frayed.

surge [SERJ] *n.* sudden, strong rush of energy
> Last night, an electrical <u>surge</u> caused a fuse to blow out at home.

woes [WOHZ] *n.* misfortunes; problems; troubles
> The lost dog's <u>woes</u> increased when it stepped on a skunk's tail.

Name _____ Date _____

Vocabulary Warm-up Exercises

Exercise A *Fill in each blank in the paragraph with an appropriate word from Word List A. Use each word only once.*

When our boss asked if we could build the shed in one day, the question seemed

[1] _____. We had never done a job that big, so we could not be sure of

the answer. Our job was made even harder by the weather. After six hours in the muggy

heat, we felt tired and [2] _____. We rejoiced when the rain finally

started. The water quickly began to [3] _____ the soil. Unfortunately, the

mud created another [4] _____ that we had to endure. Soon, we were

slipping and sliding all over the place. It was hard to maintain our

[5] _____ when we looked so ridiculous. Still, we finished the work on

time, and that really boosted our [6] _____. We had proven that we could

do the job.

Exercise B *Answer the questions with complete explanations.*

Example: Would an <u>earnest</u> speaker probably tell a lot of silly stories?
No; an <u>earnest</u> speaker is likely to be direct and serious, not silly.

1. Should <u>clarity</u> be a goal for most essay writers?

   _____

2. How are the <u>outermost</u> areas of your state different from the central regions?

   _____

3. Do you think the common cold is <u>contagious</u>?

   _____

4. Can music help to reduce someone's <u>woes</u>?

   _____

5. What might happen if there is an electrical <u>surge</u> in a computer lab?

   _____

Name _____ Date _____

Poetry Collection: Denise Levertov, William Carlos Williams,
Robert Frost, Naomi Shihab Nye
Reading Warm-up A

Read the following passage. Pay special attention to the underlined words. Then, read it again, and complete the activities. Use a separate sheet of paper for your written answers.

Spring is the season of rebirth and growth, but many poets have pointed out that it is also a time of strong contrasts. Spring rains <u>moisten</u> the ground and feed plants, but spring storms can do damage. It is a time when people enjoy the warming temperatures, but it is also a time for hard work.

In the Northern Hemisphere, spring begins with the Spring Equinox on March 21. Daylight hours increase and temperatures rise. Snows melt and plants begin to grow. Each year, spring follows this pattern, yet it is also unpredictable. During some years, people have rejoiced in early March, delighted to see buds on trees. Other years, spring drags its <u>sluggish</u> heels until late April. The arrival of spring can also mean the arrival of severe weather. Warming air patterns can lead to harsh storms and flooding. In 1993, a powerful spring blizzard dumped five feet of snow in parts of the Appalachian Mountains.

How does spring make people feel? What is the mood of spring? These questions are <u>unanswerable</u> because everyone has a unique response to spring. Indeed, you might have more than one response, depending on the day, the weather, or the events in your life. Expecting one poem to explain everything about spring is too great a <u>burden</u>. Luckily, poets have created volumes of poetry responding to this topic.

To some poets, spring is a time of natural <u>dignity</u>. They see nobility and goodness in this seasonal renewal of life. Others have taken a more critical view. Fifteenth-century poet Geoffrey Chaucer famously began his *Canterbury Tales* with a celebration of April's sweet showers. Just as famously, T. S. Eliot opened "The Waste Land" by stating that "April is the cruelest month. . . ." Each poet speaks with <u>confidence</u>, certain that his impression of spring is accurate. In the end, readers must develop their own ideas about the personal meaning of spring.

1. Circle the words that tell what will <u>moisten</u> the ground. Then, describe how you might *moisten* something else.

2. Underline the words that hint at the meaning of <u>sluggish</u>. Then, tell how someone who is *sluggish* feels.

3. Underline the words that tell why these questions are <u>unanswerable</u>. Then, describe another question you think is *unanswerable*.

4. Underline the words that describe a great <u>burden</u>. Then, describe a scene in which someone has a heavy *burden*.

5. Circle two words that are synonyms for <u>dignity</u>. Then, explain what *dignity* is.

6. Underline the words that tell why the two poets speak with <u>confidence</u>. Then, tell something about which you feel *confidence*.

Name _____ Date _____

Read the following passage. Pay special attention to the underlined words. Then, read it again, and complete the activities. Use a separate sheet of paper for your written answers.

On a typical day at noon, most of the villagers of Langore lay on blankets in the town's shady park. "We are not lazy," they would say, "we simply appreciate life." Indeed, the mood in Langore was so <u>contagious</u> that visitors quickly caught the feeling. They stopped by for lunch and ended up staying for days, resting on the blankets.

Unfortunately, very little got done in Langore and the village's <u>woes</u> began to go from bad to worse. Stores never opened because the clerks did not show up. There was no food to eat because farmers never planted crops. In fact, most land in Langore was dry as dust. The park was kept watered so the villagers had a nice place for their blankets, but the <u>outermost</u> part of town was practically a desert.

Then, one day, a stranger arrived in Langore with a broad smile and an <u>earnest</u> quality that let people know that they could trust her. Maybe that is why people still remember her first words: "You have a lovely town here, but it could use a little work."

She asked a farmer if she could work his land. He nodded absentmindedly. In an instant, the stranger had grabbed a shovel and was tossing aside the dry ground of a neglected garden, revealing rich soil underneath.

Soon villagers gathered round, watching the strange digging woman. However, it was not the digging that amazed them—it was the stranger's smile as she worked. Many people of Langore recall this as a moment of true <u>clarity</u>, when something important seemed obvious for the first time: Honest work can be both rewarding and enjoyable.

In the next weeks, a <u>surge</u> of activity erupted in Langore. People began to dig, plant, and sell. They were so busy that they did not notice when the stranger left for another town.

1. Underline the words that tell what would happen because the mood of Langore was <u>contagious</u>. Then, describe something else that is *contagious*.

2. Underline two of Langore's <u>woes</u>. Then, tell what *woes* are.

3. Circle a word that means the opposite of <u>outermost</u>. Then, tell what *outermost* means.

4. Underline the words that describe the stranger's <u>earnest</u> quality. Then, describe someone you know who is *earnest*.

5. Underline the words that explain the <u>clarity</u> of this moment. Then, tell what *clarity* means.

6. Circle the word that tells what kind of <u>surge</u> began in Langore after the stranger arrived. Then, tell what might happen if your school experienced a *surge* of creativity.

Poetry Collection: Denise Levertov, William Carlos Williams, Robert Frost,
and Naomi Shihab Nye

Literary Analysis: Narrative and Lyric Poetry

In poetry, the **speaker** is the voice that says the words of the poem. All poems have a speaker, who is either the poet or a character the poet invents to give the poem a particular voice or point of view.

- In **narrative** poetry, the speaker tells a story in verse.
- In **lyric poetry,** the speaker's thoughts, feelings, and insights create a single, unified impression. Lyric poems include **imagery,** language that appeals to the senses.

DIRECTIONS: *Answer the following questions about the poems in this collection.*

1. **A.** Who or what is the speaker in the poem "A Tree Telling of Orpheus"? _____

   B. In a few sentences, summarize the story that the speaker tells in this narrative poem.

   _____

   _____

2. Read the following lines from "Spring and All." What impression of spring does the imagery create?

   They enter the new world naked,
   cold, uncertain of all
   save that they enter.

   _____

   _____

3. Read the following lines from "Mowing." Identify four examples of imagery, and tell to which of the five senses each image appeals.

   Not without feeble-pointed spikes of flowers
   (Pale orchises), and scared a bright green snake.
   The fact is the sweetest dream that labor knows.
   My long scythe whispered and left the hay to make.

   _____

   _____

4. **A.** Who or what is the speaker in the poem "Making a Fist"? _____

   B. Summarize the story that the speaker tells in this narrative poem.

   _____

   _____

   _____

Poetry Collection: Denise Levertov, William Carlos Williams, Robert Frost, and Naomi Shihab Nye

Reading: Read Aloud and Adjust Reading Rate to Read Fluently

Read aloud to appreciate and share the musical qualities of poetry. As you read aloud, **read fluently** and **adjust your reading rate** in the following ways.

- First, read through slowly and carefully. Make sure you understand the poem's complex thoughts and that you can pronounce all the words.
- Use punctuation and group words for meaning. Do not pause at the end of a line unless a punctuation mark indicates that you should.
- Slow down to emphasize an idea or the sounds of words.

The following chart shows how to mark up a poem to help you read it fluently:

Mark the Text	Adjusting Reading Rate
Circle punctuation marks.	Pause.
Underline the words or sounds to emphasize.	Slow down.
Bracket phrases or groups of words to read together.	Speed up.

DIRECTIONS: *Write your answers to the following questions.*

1. On a separate sheet of paper, copy lines 80–85 of "A Tree Telling of Orpheus." Circle all the punctuation marks and then answer the questions.

   A. How many complete sentences do the lines contain? _____

   B. After which words should readers pause briefly?

   _____

2. Read lines 16–19 from "Spring and All." Then, follow the directions below.

   A. Underline the five adjectives a reader should emphasize when he or she reads aloud.

   B. Bracket each group of words that should be read together.

3. Read lines 3–6 of "Mowing." Then, answer the questions that follow.

   A. What five types of punctuation does the poet use in these lines?

   _____

   B. Explain how one should adjust reading rate and tone of voice for each punctuation mark.

   _____

   _____

4. Reread "Making a Fist." Explain how a reader should change his or her voice when reading the stanza with quotation marks (lines 7–11).

   _____

   _____

Name _____ Date _____

Poetry Collection: Denise Levertov, William Carlos Williams, Robert Frost, and Naomi Shihab Nye

Vocabulary Builder

Word List

anguish	clenching	idle	stark

A. DIRECTIONS: *In each item below, think about the meaning of the italicized word and then write a description that fits the meaning of the word.*

1. Describe a situation in which a person might be *clenching* his or her fists.

_____

2. Describe a *stark* scene in nature.

_____

3. Describe something a person might do during *idle* hours.

_____

4. Describe a situation in which a person might experience a feeling of *anguish*.

_____

B. DIRECTIONS: *Circle the letter of the word that best completes each sentence.*

1. When we saw the man *clenching* his jaw, we knew he was _____.
   A. happy   B. angry   C. relaxed   D. sad

2. When the machines were *idle*, the factory was _____.
   A. quiet   B. busy   C. noisy   D. profitable

3. The *stark* room was _____.
   A. cozy   B. crowded   C. overdecorated   D. uninviting

4. Her _____ face showed her *anguish*.
   A. annoyed   B. unhappy   C. excited   D. laughing

Poetry Collection: Denise Levertov, William Carlos Williams, Robert Frost, and Naomi Shihab Nye

Support for Writing a Lyric Poem

After you choose a speaker and a subject for your lyric poem, use the following graphic organizer to list imagery that describes the subject.

Subject being described: _____

Speaker in poem: _____

Now, use your notes to write a lyric poem that vividly describes the subject and conveys the speaker's feelings about it.

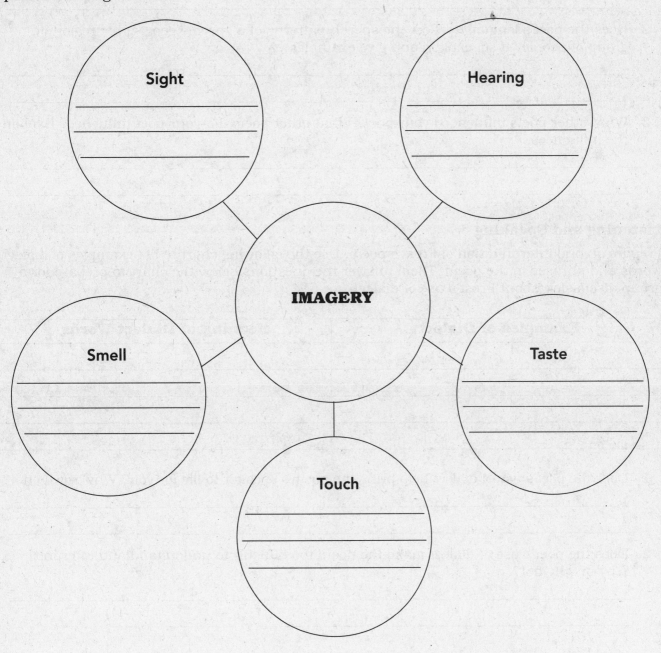

Poetry Collection: Denise Levertov, William Carlos Williams, Robert Frost,
and Naomi Shihab Nye

Support for Extend Your Learning

Research and Technology

Use the lines below to gather information for a research report. Choose one poet from this group and find information that answers the following questions about the poet's use of language.

1. How is the poet's use of language different from that of other poets?

    _____

    _____

2. Does the poet's language reflect the speech patterns of a specific geographic region or group of people? If so, explain and give examples.

    _____

    _____

3. What other poets influenced your poet? What other poets did your poet influence? Explain the influences.

    _____

    _____

Listening and Speaking

Prepare an oral interpretation of Frost's poem. Use the following chart to list examples of dialect words and phrases in the poem. Then, answer the questions below the chart to prepare for a group discussion about Frost's use of dialect.

Examples of Dialect	Meaning of Dialect Words

1. Does the poet's use of dialect help bring the poem's speaker to life for you? Why or why not?

    _____

    _____

2. Does the poet's use of dialect make the poem too difficult to understand and interpret? Why or why not?

    _____

    _____

Poetry Collection: Denise Levertov, William Carlos Williams, Robert Frost, and Naomi Shihab Nye

Enrichment: Greek Mythology

Denise Levertov's poem "A Tree Telling of Orpheus" is based on a Greek myth about Orpheus, the "father of songs." Here is how the story begins in Thomas Bullfinch's *The Age of Fable*:

> Orpheus was the son of Apollo and the Muse Calliope. He was presented by his father with a lyre and taught to play upon it, which he did to such perfection that nothing could withstand the charm of his music. Not only his fellow mortals, but wild beasts were softened by his strains, and gathering around him laid by their fierceness and stood entranced. Nay, the very trees and rocks were sensible to the charm. The trees crowded around him and the rocks relaxed somewhat of their hardness, softened by his notes.

When Orpheus's wife, Eurydice, is killed by a snakebite, Orpheus travels to the Underworld to beg Pluto, the god of the Underworld, to bring her back to life. He sings to Pluto of his love for Eurydice. Moved by Orpheus's song, Pluto allows Eurydice to return to Earth, on one condition: Orpheus must not look back at her as they journey up to Earth—or she will vanish. At the last minute, Orpheus looks back. He loses Eurydice.

Orpheus returns to Earth, heartbroken. He ignores the Thracian women, who decide to kill him. However, the beauty of his song disables their weapons. They tear him apart with their hands and bury him. His body inspires the nightingales to sing specially well. The women throw his lyre into the sky, where it becomes the constellation Lyra.

1. Which details of the myth of Orpheus does Levertov use in her poem "A Tree Telling of Orpheus"?

   _____

   _____

   _____

2. What does the myth of Orpheus reveal about how the ancient Greeks felt about music and love?

   _____

   _____

   _____

3. According to the myth, how does Orpheus live on after his death? What do these details suggest about music?

   _____

   _____

   _____

Name _____ Date _____

Build Language Skills: Vocabulary

The Latin Suffix *-ance*

The Latin suffix *-ance* means "the act or process of." It is used to form nouns. Note that if a word ends in *e*, the *e* is dropped when *-ance* is added.

> The father tried to *reassure* his children.
> His *reassurance* eased their fears.

A. DIRECTIONS: *Select a word from the box and add the suffix* -ance *to complete each sentence.*

annoy	avoid	perform	resemble

1. The mosquitoes at the barbecue were a big _____.
2. During their _____, the band played my favorite song.
3. The _____ of unhealthful snack foods will help you lose weight.
4. The twins' _____ was so strong that I could not tell them apart.

Academic Vocabulary Practice

compensate	diverse	radical	significance	visual

B. DIRECTIONS: *Think about the meaning of each italicized word below. Then, write a sentence that answers the question.*

1. What *radical* change would you like to see in your community's government?

   _____

2. Why is it important for people with *diverse* opinions to communicate?

   _____

3. What might be a *visual* way to describe a freshly baked apple pie?

   _____

4. Explain the *significance* of one event that has occurred in the United States this year.

   _____

5. How might you *compensate* people for accidentally damaging their property?

   _____

Name _____ Date _____

Poetry Collections: Maxim Pushkin, Federico García Lorca, Elizabeth Bishop, Rudyard Kipling; Denise Levertov, William Carlos Williams, Robert Frost, and Naomi Shihab Nye

Build Language Skills: Grammar

Preposition and Object of Preposition

A **preposition** is a word that relates a noun or pronoun that appears with it to another word in the sentence. Common prepositions are *across*, *against*, *at*, *of*, *on*, *to*, *under*, and *with*. The following sentence includes two prepositional phrases. Each preposition is underlined once, and each object is underlined twice.

<u>On</u> the <u>table</u>, there is a scrapbook filled <u>with</u> some <u>letters</u> and <u>photographs</u>.

A. DIRECTIONS: *Draw a circle around each prepositional phrase in the sentences. Then, underline the preposition once and the object, or objects, of the preposition twice.*

1. I bought a birthday gift for Alex.
2. Abraham Lincoln was the President of the United States during the Civil War.
3. Last night there was a ring around the moon.
4. Among my favorite possessions is an antique ring from my grandmother.
5. Did you go to the dance after the game?
6. The girl on the left is my cousin Jenna.
7. The object of the game is guessing the answer to the riddle.
8. Move the table toward the wall.
9. Earth is located between Mars and Venus.
10. Walking with the ball in your hands is against the rules of the game.

B. DIRECTIONS: *Write a paragraph describing your favorite place. Describe the details of the place in spatial order, using prepositions such as* across, above, behind, in front of, near, next to, on, *and* under.

_____

_____

_____

_____

_____

Name _____   Date _____

Poetry Collection by Denise Levertov, William Carlos Williams,
Robert Frost, and Naomi Shihab Nye
Selection Test A

Critical Reading *Identify the letter of the choice that best answers the question.*

___ 1. Why is "A Tree Telling of Orpheus" considered a narrative poem?
   A. because it has a speaker
   B. because it tells a story
   C. because it creates a single impression
   D. because it is so long

___ 2. At the beginning of "A Tree Telling of Orpheus," what causes the strange new "rippling" feeling the tree has?
   A. the sun
   B. the wind
   C. a man's song
   D. a woman's laugh

___ 3. What do the experiences described in "A Tree Telling of Orpheus" show about life?
   A. the power of music
   B. the effects of weather
   C. the goodness of nature
   D. the wisdom of stillness

___ 4. Why is "Spring and All" considered a lyric poem?
   A. because it has a speaker
   B. because it tells a story
   C. because it creates a single impression
   D. because it is so short

___ 5. How should the following lines from "Spring and All" be read aloud?
      They enter the new world naked,
      cold, uncertain of all
      save that they enter.
   A. Do not pause at all.
   B. Pause at the end of each line.
   C. Pause after *world, naked,* and *enter.*
   D. Pause after *naked, cold,* and *enter.*

____ 6. What feeling is conveyed by the imagery in "Spring and All"?
   A. cheerfulness
   B. uncertainty
   C. regret
   D. anger

____ 7. What does the speaker describe in "Mowing"?
   A. the frustration of not having good tools
   B. the companionship of working with others
   C. the rewards of doing hard work outdoors
   D. the dream of leaving farmwork behind

____ 8. To which of the five senses does the following imagery from "Mowing" appeal?
   My long scythe whispered and left the hay to make.
   A. sight and hearing
   B. sight and touch
   C. hearing and touch
   D. hearing and smell

____ 9. How many sentences would be included if the following lines from "Mowing" were read aloud?
   There was never a sound beside the wood but one,
   And that was my long scythe whispering to the ground.
   A. none
   B. one
   C. two
   D. three

____ 10. How old was the speaker of "Making a Fist" when she begged her mother to answer an important question?
   A. seven
   B. sixteen
   C. twenty-five
   D. forty

____ 11. Why is the speaker of "Making a Fist" still clenching her hand?
   A. Sometimes she still needs to prove to herself that she's alive.
   B. Sometimes she wants to remember how foolish her mother was.
   C. Sometimes she forgets why her parents took her on a trip.
   D. Sometimes she gets tired from too much traveling.

_____ 12. What message about life does "Making a Fist" convey?

    A. Parents can make mistakes when they answer children's questions.

    B. Children can be annoying when they ask too many questions.

    C. People will say that life is a lot easier than we think it is.

    D. Everyone needs quiet strength to survive life's challenges.

Vocabulary and Grammar

_____ 13. In which season of the year is a forest most likely to look very *stark*?

    A. summer

    B. winter

    C. spring

    D. fall

_____ 14. Which item below is a thing of great *significance*?

    A. a war

    B. a magnet

    C. a map

    D. a car

_____ 15. Which sentence does NOT include a prepositional phrase?

    A. I went to the store for some eggs.

    B. The letter from Hank was funny.

    C. I went swimming here yesterday.

    D. The woman on the right is Sarah.

Essay

16. Choose one of the narrative poems in this group and write a brief essay summarizing the story it tells. Explain the setting, who the main characters are, and three or four important events in the narrative.

17. Which of the four poems do you think creates the strongest emotional impression or expresses the strongest feelings? In a brief essay, describe the feeling the poem conveys. Then, explain how the poet uses vivid descriptions or a dramatic story to create this feeling.

Poetry Collection by Denise Levertov, William Carlos Williams, Robert Frost, and Naomi Shihab Nye

Selection Test B

Critical Reading *Identify the letter of the choice that best answers the question.*

____ 1. Why is "A Tree Telling of Orpheus" considered a narrative poem?
   A. It has strong visual imagery.
   B. It has characters and a plot.
   C. It is more than a hundred lines long.
   D. It has no speaker.

____ 2. Which statement best describes "A Tree Telling of Orpheus"?
   A. It is a fable with a moral about passing time.
   B. It is an imaginative re-creation of a true event.
   C. It is a classical myth about a powerful musician.
   D. It is an account of the birth of music and fire.

____ 3. In "A Tree Telling of Orpheus," why is it effective to use a tree as the speaker?
   A. It causes us to find the story of Orpheus more believable.
   B. It gives the poem a lighthearted feeling because of its impossibility.
   C. It allows us to imagine Orpheus's power more vividly.
   D. It explains the unusual arrangement of the poem's line breaks.

____ 4. Which words should be emphasized in these lines from Levertov's poem?
   Music! There was no twig of me not / trembling with joy and fear.

   A. *music, me, trembling*
   B. *music, joy, fear*
   C. *twig, trembling, fear*
   D. *no, not, trembling*

____ 5. What is the speaker describing in the following lines from "Spring and All"?
   They enter the new world naked, / cold, uncertain of all / save that they enter.

   A. infants lying in a hospital nursery
   B. bear cubs awakening in a cave
   C. butterflies emerging from a cocoon
   D. sprouting plants along a roadside

____ 6. Which sense is most appealed to in the imagery of "Spring and All"?
   A. sight
   B. hearing
   C. sound
   D. smell

____ 7. What is the insight offered as the theme of "Spring and All"?
   A. Living things constantly struggle against disease.
   B. Life can survive even in an apparently bleak landscape.
   C. Growth can be shocking in its sudden explosiveness.
   D. Strong contrasts exist between human and plant life.

Name _____ Date _____

_____ 8. How can "Spring and All" best be described?
   A. It is a lyric poem with a mood of uncertainty and determination.
   B. It is a lyric poem with a mood of anger and despair.
   C. It is a narrative poem about a man's search for inner peace.
   D. It is a narrative poem about a doctor's patient who is dying.

_____ 9. Who is the speaker of "Mowing"?
   A. a farmer who loves hard work
   B. a doctor who enjoys lawn care
   C. a teenager who hates weekend chores
   D. a child who imitates his father

_____ 10. In "Mowing," what is the one sound the speaker hears?
   A. the roar of his lawn mower
   B. the quiet motion of his scythe
   C. the musical chirp of a bird
   D. the puff of each of his breaths

_____ 11. Which of the following lines best supports the theme of "Mowing"?
   A. "There was never a sound beside the wood but one,"
   B. "It was no dream of the gift of idle hours,"
   C. "The fact is the sweetest dream that nature knows."
   D. "Perhaps it was something about the heat of the sun,"

_____ 12. Which words should you emphasize when reading these lines from "Mowing" aloud?
   Anything more than the truth would have seemed too weak
   To the earnest love that laid the swale in rows,

   A. *more, too, earnest*
   B. *Anything, seemed, laid*
   C. *truth, laid, swale*
   D. *truth, weak, love*

_____ 13. Who is the speaker in "Making a Fist"?
   A. a child dreaming of her future life as an adult
   B. a woman recalling an incident from her childhood
   C. a mother remembering her daughter's curiosity
   D. a neutral outsider observing a mother and her child

_____ 14. Why does the speaker of "Making a Fist" continue to clench her hand?
   A. She still feels angry at her mother for deceiving her.
   B. She never really grew up and is quite immature.
   C. She still needs to prove to herself that she's alive.
   D. She wishes she were still a child protected by her parents.

_____ 15. What message is expressed by both "Spring and All" and "Making a Fist"?
   A. People can be alienated from their natural surroundings.
   B. People often do not appreciate life until it is nearly over.
   C. Life is never really as difficult as we think it is.
   D. Life is a process involving struggle and uncertainty.

_____ 16. How should these lines from "Making a Fist" be read aloud?

> I was seven, I lay in the car / watching palm trees swirl in a sickening pattern / past the glass.

    A. Do not pause at all.
    B. Pause at the end of each line.
    C. Pause after *seven* and *glass.*
    D. Pause after *car* and *glass.*

Vocabulary and Grammar

_____ 17. Why does the tree speaking in "A Tree Telling of Orpheus" feel *anguish*?
    A. It is delighted that the music is beautiful.
    B. It is distressed that Orpheus is leaving.
    C. It is surprised that a man makes music.
    D. It is amused that Orpheus sings to trees.

_____ 18. Which of the following scenes could best be described as *stark*?
    A. a flower garden in summer
    B. a park during fall foliage time
    C. a lake in late spring
    D. a forest in the middle of winter

_____ 19. In the following sentence, which word is the object of the preposition *to*?

> There was a sticker glued to the back of the picture frame.

    A. sticker
    B. back
    C. picture
    D. frame

_____ 20. Which sentence does NOT have a preposition?
    A. The huge movie screen is awe-inspiring.
    B. I'm eating lunch with several friends.
    C. People often debate about politics.
    D. Can you lift that weight above your head?

Essay

21. The poems in this group explore powerful themes about music, growth, death, and work. In an essay, discuss the theme, or message about life, that is conveyed in one of the poems. Explain how the poet uses imagery or a dramatic narrative to convey this theme.

22. In a brief essay, identify one lyric poem and one narrative poem from the group. Summarize the main impression or the story conveyed in each poem. Then, describe your response to each poem and tell which lyric or narrative elements you especially enjoyed.

23. In "A Tree Telling of Orpheus," a tree speaks to us in the first person. In a brief essay, evaluate the risks and rewards of using a nonhuman speaker to narrate events. For example, does such a speaker make the poem seem childish and unbelievable? Or does the speaker startle readers into a fresh appreciation of something? Support your judgment with examples from the poem.

Vocabulary Warm-up Word Lists

*Study these words from the poetry of Toshiyori, Tsurayuki, Johnson, and Thomas. Then, apply
your knowledge to the activities that follow.*

Word List A

avenues [AV uh nooz] *n.* streets in a town or city
His neighborhood has lovely wide <u>avenues</u> lined with shade trees.

brighter [BRY ter] *adj.* lighter; more shiny
The front room is <u>brighter</u> than the kitchen because it has more windows.

fierce [FEERS] *adj.* showing anger that is extreme or severe
The barking of the <u>fierce</u> dog terrified the small children.

gentle [JEN tuhl] *adj.* not strong or violent
The sound of my mother's <u>gentle</u> voice helped soothe me to sleep.

patient [PAY shuhnt] *adj.* able to wait calmly for a long time
It was hard to remain <u>patient</u> after waiting in line for over an hour.

throbbing [THRAH bing] *v.* beating strongly and regularly
My head kept <u>throbbing</u> to the beat of the music after the concert ended.

Word List B

clustering [KLUS tuhr ing] *v.* gathering; forming in a group
Soon, the children were all <u>clustering</u> around the darling kitten.

grieved [GREEVD] *v.* having felt extremely sad
The entire family <u>grieved</u> the death of their beloved, loyal dog.

stark [STAHRK] *adj.* grim; harsh
Despite a childhood spent in <u>stark</u> poverty, she later became wealthy.

subtile or **subtle** [SUHT l] *adj.* not easily noticed unless one pays close attention
Ken was quick to notice her <u>subtle</u> charms so often overlooked by others.

threshold [THRESH ohld] *n.* the base of a doorway; entrance; a point of beginning
We are crossing a <u>threshold</u> into a new era in world relations.

unutterable [un uh ter uh buhl] *adj.* difficult to express because of the greatness of
emotion
She felt <u>unutterable</u> sadness when her favorite climbing oak was cut down.

Name _____ Date _____

Vocabulary Warm-up Exercises

Exercise A *Fill in each blank in the paragraph with an appropriate word from Word List A. Use each word only once.*

Not everyone loves a big city. Newcomers are sometimes amazed at how

[1] _____ city dwellers seem while they wait in endless lines for just

about everything. While some people love the [2] _____ music of enter-

tainers playing in the subways, it gives other people headaches. Tourists might enjoy

the energy of rush hour, while others dislike the [3] _____ competition

of commuters jostling for a spot on a subway train. Almost everyone can appreciate

window shopping while walking on the wide [4] _____ of a downtown

shopping area. Yet to some, the sunshine will always be [5] _____

when it is not blocked by skyscrapers. They will always prefer the calmer, more

[6] _____ pleasures of life in the country.

Exercise B *Answer the questions with complete explanations.*

1. Would <u>clustering</u> weeds grow scattered in isolated spots?

   _____

2. If your friend <u>grieved</u> after hearing some news, would you expect that she would be happy?

   _____

3. If people live in <u>stark</u> conditions, do you think they have lots of material comforts?

   _____

4. If you praise someone's <u>subtle</u> wit, would you expect that everyone could appreciate his or her humor?

   _____

5. If you are standing on the <u>threshold</u> of a career in journalism, are you already working as a journalist?

   _____

6. If you feel <u>unutterable</u> sadness at a tragedy, would you speak about it to all of your friends?

   _____

Poetry Collection: Minamoto no Toshiyori, Ki Tsurayuki,
James Weldon Johnson, and Dylan Thomas

Reading Warm-up A

Read the following passage. Pay special attention to the underlined words. Then, read it again, and complete the activities. Use a separate sheet of paper for your written answers.

Dylan Thomas was an astonishingly good writer. His work has moved many since his early death at only 39 years old. Indeed, Thomas's work is often adapted for new projects. For example, his Christmas story, "A Child's Christmas in Wales" has been adapted into movies and plays. In this story, Thomas presents a childhood when the light shone <u>brighter</u> and even the snow seemed better. This nostalgic story remains a holiday favorite. The famous 1960s singer Donovan, recorded a song using the words from Thomas's poem "Do Not Go Gentle" as its lyrics. However, it would be hard for anyone to beat Thomas's own <u>throbbing</u> voice in a reading of the poem. Thomas's radio play *Under Milk Wood* has been made into a movie. It is still produced often as a stage play.

Thomas's poetry and life have inspired painters and composers, too. John Selway, a British artist, used themes from Thomas's poetry in a series of paintings. The <u>patient</u> fans of John Corigliano waited years for the classical composer to complete "A Dylan Thomas Choral Trilogy." This work is based on three of Thomas's most famous poems. The music reflects the poetry of this sometimes <u>gentle</u>, sometimes <u>fierce</u> genius.

Dylan Thomas's life continues to fascinate. The Chelsea Hotel, on 23ʳᵈ Street between Ninth and Tenth <u>Avenues</u> in New York City, still advertises that Dylan Thomas lived there more than 50 years ago. Many biographies have been written about him. In 1990, the actor Anthony Hopkins directed a movie about Thomas's tours in the United States, which is called *Return Journey*.

The influence of Dylan Thomas is also apparent in other areas. Some critics believe that the well-known musician Bob Dylan changed his last name from Zimmerman to honor the Welsh poet. In fact, the name Dylan, which was rare when Thomas was born, is one of the most popular names for boys in the United States today.

1. Circle the word that tells what shone <u>brighter</u> in childhood. Then, explain what *brighter* means.

2. Circle the word that tells whose voice is <u>throbbing</u> in a reading of "Do Not Go Gentle Into That Good Night." Then, tell what *throbbing* means.

3. Underline the words that give a clue to the meaning of <u>patient</u>. Use *patient* in a sentence.

4. Circle the word that means the opposite of <u>gentle</u>. Use *gentle* in a sentence.

5. Who is the "<u>fierce</u> genius" whose work is reflected in Corigliano's music? Rewrite the sentence with *fierce* in it, replacing *fierce* with a synonym.

6. Circle the name of the <u>avenues</u> near the Chelsea Hotel. Write the names of some of your own favorite *avenues*. Describe them.

Poetry Collection: Minamoto no Toshiyori, Ki Tsurayuki,
James Weldon Johnson, and Dylan Thomas

Reading Warm-up B

Read the following passage. Pay special attention to the underlined words. Then, read it again, and complete the activities. Use a separate sheet of paper for your written answers.

As one of the major writers associated with the Harlem Renaissance, it is no wonder that James Weldon Johnson wrote a love poem to his city. It was there that he crossed the <u>threshold</u> from relative obscurity into the world of fame and success. Johnson wrote an entire book entitled *Black Manhattan,* which told about the cultural contributions of African Americans in New York City. He lived in his beloved New York for many years. While there, he did everything from working for civil rights to writing lyrics for the theater. He also found time to write poetry and a novel and to encourage talented young African American writers such as Langston Hughes and Claude McKay.

At that time, African American artists and professionals began <u>clustering</u> in the neighborhood known as Harlem. Johnson championed these artists in many ways. For example, he edited a collection of poetry by African Americans. This book showcased both the obvious and the <u>subtle</u> attractions of the poets.

James Weldon Johnson also wrote lyrics for songs that his brother, J. Rosamond Johnson, composed. Their most famous song is called "Lift Every Voice and Sing." They wrote this song for children to sing at a birthday celebration for Abraham Lincoln. The song became popular nationwide, and it became known as the "Negro National Anthem." The lyrics tell of African Americans moving from the painful, <u>stark</u> conditions of the past into a more hope-filled present and future.

As one of the shapers of the National Association for the Advancement of Colored People (NAACP), Johnson fought against the <u>unutterable</u> injustice and racism that existed all over the United States. As the head of the organization, he helped to greatly increase its membership. "Lift Every Voice and Sing" became the anthem for the NAACP, and it is still sung at meetings today.

Many admirers <u>grieved</u> when Johnson died in a tragic car accident in Maine in 1938. Decades later, his life and his work continue to inspire us.

1. Underline the phrase that tells what Johnson found after crossing the <u>threshold</u> from obscurity. Explain what *threshold* means.

2. Explain why African Americans might have begun <u>clustering</u> in the Harlem neighborhood. Write a synonym for *clustering*.

3. Circle the word that means the opposite of <u>subtle</u>. Then, use *subtle* in a sentence.

4. Explain why the history of African Americans before 1900 could be described as <u>stark</u>. What else could you describe as *stark*?

5. Circle two things that the narrator describes as <u>unutterable</u>. How else might you describe these things?

6. Circle words that are clues to the meaning of <u>grieved</u>. Write a sentence telling about something or someone you have *grieved*.

Name _____ Date _____

Literary Analysis: Poetic Form

To unify sounds and ideas in a poem, a poet may follow a **poetic form,** or a defined structure. Each poetic form uses a set number of lines. Some have a unique **meter,** or rhythm, and a unique pattern of **rhymes.** In your textbook, review the traditional poetic form. Then, complete the exercise.

DIRECTIONS: *Answer the following questions about the poems in this collection.*

1. Both "When I went to visit. . ." and "The clustering clouds. . ." are translations of Japanese poems. Count the syllables in each line of the two poems. Which translation provides a better example of the tanka form? Why?

    _____

    _____

2. Read aloud the first four lines of the poem "My City." Then, answer the following questions.

    When I come down to sleep death's endless night,
       The threshold of the unknown dark to cross,
       What to me then will be the keenest loss,
    When this bright world blurs on my fading sight?

    A. Above each unaccented syllable, draw a ˘ . Above each accented syllable, draw a ´.

    B. How many accented and unaccented syllables did you find in each line?

    _____

    C. What is the rhyme scheme of the lines? _____

    D. In what poetic form is "My City" written? _____

3. Read aloud the first two stanzas of "Do Not Go Gentle Into That Good Night." Then, answer the following questions.

    Do not go gentle into that good night,
    Old age should burn and rave at close of day;
    Rage, rage against the dying of the light.

    Though wise men at their end know dark is right,
    Because their words had forked no lightning they
    Do not go gentle into that good night.

    A. How many lines are in each stanza? _____

    B. What is the rhyme scheme of the two stanzas? _____

    C. Which line is repeated? _____

    D. In what poetic form is the poem written? _____

Poetry Collection: Ki Tsurayuki, Minamoto no Toshiyori, James Weldon Johnson, and Dylan Thomas

Reading: Preview a Poem to Read Fluently

When you **read fluently,** you read smoothly and with understanding. You place emphasis appropriately and pause where necessary. To increase your fluency when reading a poem, **preview** the work. Look over the text in advance:

- Use footnotes and other text aids to learn unfamiliar words.
- Determine where each sentence in the poem begins and ends. Pause only when the punctuation indicates you should.
- Form a rough idea of the topic and mood of the work. Read the poem with its mood in mind.

DIRECTIONS: *Answer the following questions about the poems in this collection.*

1. Preview the poem "When I went to visit. . . ." What three punctuation marks do you see in the poem?

   _____

2. Preview the poem "The clustering clouds. . . ." How can the punctuation marks help you read the poem smoothly and with understanding?

   _____

3. Preview the poem "My City" and answer the questions.

   A. How many end marks do you find in lines 1–8? _____

   B. How do the end marks in lines 1–8 differ?

   _____

   C. How do these end marks determine the way you should read lines 1–8 for understanding?

   _____

   _____

   D. What end mark is used twice in lines 9–14?

   E. How does the end mark affect how you should read lines 9–14?

   _____

4. Preview the poem "Do Not Go Gentle Into That Good Night." Then, answer the questions.

   A. In stanzas 1–5, how many sentences does each stanza contain? _____

   B. How does the number of sentences in stanzas 1–5 help you read each stanza fluently?

   _____

   C. What word is repeated at the beginning of lines 3, 9, 15, and 19? _____

   D. How does this repetition offer a clue to the overall mood you should convey when reading the poem?

   _____

Poetry Collection: Ki Tsurayuki, Minamoto no Toshiyori, James Weldon Johnson, and Dylan Thomas

Vocabulary Builder

Word List

| clustering | frail | lunar | threshold |

A. DIRECTIONS: *Write whether each statement is* true *or* false. *Explain why.*

_____ 1. *Clustering* birds are a common sight in autumn.

_____

_____ 2. A *lunar* eclipse is an eclipse of the sun.

_____

_____ 3. Many homes have chimneys on their *thresholds*.

_____

_____ 4. A *frail* person should not try ice skating.

_____

B. DIRECTIONS: *Choose the best* **antonym** *for each word.*

1. clustering
   A. gathering
   B. stacking
   C. separating
   D. arguing
2. threshold
   A. ending
   B. grip
   C. entrance
   D. height
3. frail
   A. tiny
   B. sick
   C. beautiful
   D. strong

Name _____ Date _____

Support for Writing a Tanka

Before drafting your tanka, read the simple example below. Then, draft your own tanka on the blank lines. Use only the number of syllables indicated for each line. In your poem, you might want to describe your response to a specific type of weather.

Subject: Lying in bed listening to a storm outside

Mood: Cozy, thankful

Rain beats the windows.	**5 syllables**
Wind howls and sneaks through the cracks.	**7 syllables**
I smile with content.	**5 syllables**
Their fury cannot touch me.	**7 syllables**
I am snug and warm in bed.	**7 syllables**

Subject of Your Poem: _____

Mood You Want to Convey: _____

5 syllables _____

7 syllables _____

5 syllables _____

7 syllables _____

7 syllables _____

Poetry Collection: Ki Tsurayuki, Minamoto no Toshiyori, James Weldon Johnson, and Dylan Thomas

Support for Extended Learning

Research and Technology

Use the lines below to gather information for a visual presentation on Japanese art.

Aspects of nature described in "When I went to visit . . ." and "The clustering clouds . . .":

_____

Mood conveyed by the two tanka poems:

_____

Artworks That Could Illustrate the Poems:

Image 1:   Title: _____

How artwork relates to poems: _____

Description of artistic style: _____

Image 2:   Title: _____

How artwork relates to poems: _____

Description of artistic style: _____

Listening and Speaking

Use the chart to take notes for a discussion as you listen to a recording of Dylan Thomas reading "Do Not Go Gentle Into That Good Night."

Speed of reading	
Tone of voice	
Words he emphasizes	
Where he pauses	
How he express rhythm/rhyme	

Poetry Collection: Ki Tsurayuki, Minamoto no Toshiyori, James Weldon Johnson, and Dylan Thomas

Enrichment: Poetry in Ancient Japanese Culture

The tanka is the most widespread poetic form found in traditional Japanese literature. During the years A.D. 794–1185, every educated young man and woman was expected to be able to write beautiful tanka to mark important occasions and personal experiences. Writing tanka was so popular that the government held poetry contests and published the best entries. Tanka were often exchanged with friends, the way we exchange notes and e-mail messages today.

The form and content of tanka reflect traditional Japanese values. For example, the tanka's focus on nature comes from the traditional Japanese religion Shintoism. Shintoism teaches that mountains, streams, lakes, and other elements of nature are inhabited by spirits, known as *kami.* To live a good life, a person must live in harmony with nature. One can gain wisdom and understanding by thinking deeply about the natural world.

Traditionally, the Japanese have preferred simple, quiet observations over complicated or showy statements. Instead of pouring out their feelings in long, detailed letters describing every aspect of their troubles and relationships, the Japanese wrote tanka. They hinted at their feelings through a few powerful images from nature.

DIRECTIONS: *Apply the information above to the two tanka in this collection by answering the following questions.*

1. In the two tanka you have read, how do the poets convey a sense of spiritual harmony with nature?

   _____

   _____

   _____

   _____

2. How does the tanka "When I went to visit . . ." reflect the traditional Japanese values of suggestion and restraint in describing personal relationships?

   _____

   _____

   _____

3. Do you think it is more interesting to read literature that hints at a feeling, as a tanka does, or literature that describes feelings in detail? Give two reasons for your answer.

Poetry Collection: Ki Tsurayuki, Minamoto no Toshiyori, James Weldon Johnson, and Dylan Thomas

Selection Test A

Critical Reading *Identify the letter of the choice that best answers the question.*

____ 1. Which of the following are characteristics of the tanka form?
   A. 14 lines and 5 accented syllables per line
   B. a rhyme scheme of *aba*
   C. 5 lines and a syllable count of 5, 7, 5, 7, 7
   D. a rhyme scheme of *abba, cddc, efef, gg*

____ 2. What does the tanka "When I went to visit . . ." describe?
   A. a warm summer afternoon
   B. a cold winter night
   C. a flowering tree in spring
   D. migrating birds in the fall

____ 3. What does the speaker of "When I went to visit . . ." hint at, or suggest, in the poem?
   A. how deeply he loves his girlfriend
   B. how greatly he regrets his actions
   C. how cruelly his beloved treats him
   D. how cleverly he tricked someone

____ 4. In "The clustering clouds . . .," what image does the speaker contrast with the clouds?
   A. sunlight
   B. moonlight
   C. snowflakes
   D. raindrops

____ 5. When previewing the following lines from "The clustering clouds . . .," where should readers plan to pause?
   Can it be they wipe away
   The lunar shadows?
   A. after the word *be*
   B. after the word *away*
   C. after the word *shadows*
   D. after the words *away* and *shadows*

___ 6. Which of the following characteristics belong to the sonnet form?

    A. 14 lines, regular rhythm and rhyme

    B. 5 lines, strict syllable count

    C. 19 lines, six stanzas

    D. 16 lines, no pattern of rhythm or rhyme

___ 7. What will the speaker of "My City" most regret losing when he dies?

    A. the brightness of the world

    B. the experience of city life

    C. the touch of people he loves

    D. the sound of children's voices

___ 8. When previewing the following lines from "My City," how many sentences should readers plan to read fluently?

    When I come down to sleep death's endless night,

      The threshold of the unknown dark to cross,

      What to me then will be the keenest loss,

    When this bright world blurs on my fading sight?

    A. none

    B. one

    C. two

    D. four

___ 9. In the following line from "My City," how many beats, or accented syllables, are there?

    Her crowds, her throbbing force, the thrill that comes

    A. three

    B. four

    C. five

    D. six

___ 10. In "Do Not Go Gentle Into That Good Night," what advice does the speaker give to old people?

    A. Accept death with grace and dignity.

    B. Hold on fiercely to each moment of your life.

    C. Protect yourself from a dangerous world.

    D. Pass wisdom to those who come after you.

____ 11. What is the rhyme scheme of the following lines from "Do Not Go Gentle Into That Good Night"?

> Do not go gentle into that good night,
> Old age should burn and rave at close of day;
> Rage, rage against the dying of the light.

A. *aba*

B. *abb*

C. *aab*

D. *abc*

____ 12. Whom does the speaker address in the last stanza of "Do Not Go Gentle Into That Good Night"?

A. his wife

B. his daughter

C. his father

D. his son

Vocabulary and Grammar

____ 13. Where is the *threshold* of your home?

A. on the roof

C. at the back window

B. at the front door

D. in the bedroom

____ 14. What does the *significance* of an event refer to?

A. its location

C. its importance

B. its length

D. its different parts

____ 15. Which sentence includes a direct object?

A. I went to the grocery store.

B. I bought some plants.

C. The aisles were crowded.

D. I ran to the express lane.

Essay

16. Which poem in this group did you find most interesting or surprising? In a brief essay, describe how the poem's subject matter and form contributed to your enjoyment. In addition to telling what the poem is about, discuss its length and its stanzas (if any), any memorable images it includes, and any pattern of rhythm and rhyme that you found interesting.

17. Both "My City" and "Do Not Go Gentle Into That Good Night" use verse to present a point of view about death. Choose one of the poems. Choose one of the poems, and discuss the speaker's opinion of dying. Include reasons the speaker gives for his viewpoint.

Name _____ Date _____

Poetry Collection: Ki Tsurayuki, Minamoto no Toshiyori, James Weldon Johnson,
and Dylan Thomas

Selection Test B

Critical Reading *Identify the letter of the choice that best completes the statement or answers
the question.*

____ 1. How is the tanka form mainly identified?
  A. by its length and imagery
  B. by its rhythm and rhyme
  C. by its rhythm and imagery
  D. by its length and rhyme

____ 2. What does the tanka form usually include?
  A. a long description of natural events
  B. a long description of the speaker's feelings
  C. one line that tells the poem's meaning
  D. one image that suggests the speaker's feelings

____ 3. When previewing "When I went to visit. . .," which of the following should readers notice?
  A. Each line is a separate sentence.
  B. There are no sentences in the five lines.
  C. There are two sentences in the five lines.
  D. The five lines form one complete sentence.

____ 4. Why does the speaker of "When I went to visit. . ." describe the weather?
  A. to suggest how much he hates winter
  B. to suggest his love for his girlfriend
  C. to suggest his regret over his actions
  D. to suggest how cold his heart has turned

____ 5. On which conflict does "The clustering clouds. . ." focus?
  A. winter and summer
  B. clouds and sunshine
  C. shadows and moonlight
  D. daytime and nighttime

____ 6. What is one of the ways you can tell that "My City" is a sonnet?
  A. It has 14 lines and 5 unaccented and accented words per line.
  B. It has 14 lines, 5 accented syllables per line, and no rhyme.
  C. It has 19 lines, six stanzas, and a rhyme scheme.
  D. It has 19 lines, along with lines and rhymes that repeat.

____ 7. Which characteristic of a sonnet is evident in the following lines from "My City"?
    When I come down to sleep death's endless night,
      The threshold of the unknown dark to cross,
  A. couplet
  B. rhyme scheme
  C. accent pattern
  D. repetition

____ 8. What seems to be the speaker's main point in "My City"?
   A. how much he fears his death
   B. how peaceful he feels about life
   C. how bored he is by nature
   D. how much he loves a place

____ 9. When previewing the following lines from "My City," how many sentences should readers plan to read fluently?

   > Will it be that no more I shall see the trees
   >   Or smell the flowers or hear the singing birds
   >   Or watch the flashing streams or patient herds?
   > No, I am sure it will be none of these.

   A. one
   B. two
   C. three
   D. four

____ 10. In "Do Not Go Gentle Into That Good Night," what advice does the speaker give to older people?
   A. Accept death with grace and dignity.
   B. Try not to regret the things you did not do.
   C. Hold on fiercely to each moment of your life.
   D. Set a good example for your children.

____ 11. Which word is repeated most often in "Do Not Go Gentle Into That Good Night"?
   A. life
   B. death
   C. rage
   D. weep

____ 12. Which characteristics make "Do Not Go Gentle Into That Good Night" a good example of the villanelle form?
   A. 14 lines, 5 accented words per line, rhyme scheme
   B. 14 lines, 5 syllables per line, repeated lines
   C. 19 lines, 6 stanzas, repeated lines
   D. 19 lines, a 2-line summary, rhyme scheme

____ 13. When previewing "Do Not Go Gentle Into That Good Night," what should readers notice about stanzas 1–5?
   A. Each stanza is one complete sentence.
   B. Each stanza is two complete sentences.
   C. Each line has no pauses within it.
   D. Each line has several pauses within it.

____ 14. How are "My City" and "Do Not Go Gentle Into That Good Night" similar?
   A. They have the same rhyme scheme.
   B. They have lines that repeat several times.
   C. They express an opinion about death.
   D. They celebrate the variety of urban life.

____ **15.** What is a correct generalization about the three poetic forms in this group?

    A. The tanka emphasizes rhyme more than the sonnet and the villanelle.

    B. The sonnet and the villanelle emphasize rhyme more than the tanka.

    C. The tanka emphasizes length more than the sonnet and the villanelle.

    D. The sonnet and the villanelle emphasize imagery more than the tanka.

Vocabulary and Grammar

____ **16.** In the following lines from "My City," what does the word *threshold* refer to?

> When I come down to sleep death's endless night,
>> The *threshold* of the unknown dark to cross,

    A. the front door of the speaker's house

    B. the entrance to a dark room

    C. the change from waking to sleeping

    D. the passage from life to death

____ **17.** In "Do Not Go Gentle Into That Good Night," what does "*frail* deeds" refer to?

    A. powerful actions   **C.** well-meaning actions

    B. weak actions   **D.** cruel actions

____ **18.** What is another way to describe *diverse* interpretations of a poem?

    A. They are different interpretations.

    B. They are similar interpretations.

    C. They are correct interpretations.

    D. They are incorrect interpretations.

____ **19.** Which sentence does NOT include a direct object?

    A. We saw interesting exhibits at the museum.

    B. A guide told us facts about the artwork.

    C. We are planning another visit soon.

    D. I want to go again soon with my friends.

Essay

20. Both "My City" and "Do Not Go Gentle Into That Good Night" use verse to present a particular point of view. In a brief essay, compare and contrast each speaker's opinion about dying. Then offer at least two reasons given by each speaker supporting his point of view.

21. A tanka suggests deep feelings in a few brief lines. Sonnets and villanelles, on the other hand, include many lines and details to elaborate on a feeling or thought. In your opinion, which of the three forms creates the most powerful, lasting effect on readers? Choose the poem in this group that had the strongest emotional effect on you. In a brief essay, describe its impact. Use at least two details from the poem to explain how its form and content help create that impact.

22. In "Do Not Go Gentle Into That Good Night," Dylan Thomas advises old people near death to "rage, rage against the dying of the light." He asks his father to "curse, bless me now with your fierce tears, I pray." In a brief essay, evaluate Thomas's advice. Explain why you think his view of dying is wise or unwise. Analyze how a dying person such as his father might respond to the advice. In your essay, give two or three reasons why you agree or disagree with Thomas's point of view. Use details from the poem to support your position.

Vocabulary Warm-up Word Lists

Study these words from the poetry of Jakuren, Komachi, Roethke, and Shakespeare. Then, apply your knowledge to the activities that follow.

Word List A

being [BEE ing] *n.* someone's whole self or the essence of the self
   It seemed as if the force of the infant's entire <u>being</u> went into its wailing.

compare [kuhm PAIR] *v.* to examine or judge two or more things in order to show how they are similar to or different from each other
   We will <u>compare</u> the features of the two laptops before deciding which to buy.

lowly [LOH lee] *adj.* low in rank or importance
   The <u>lowly</u> intern started each day by making coffee for the executives.

nature [NAY chuhr] *n.* everything that exists in the world that is not made by humans, such as animals, plants, weather, and so on.
   Powerful tsunamis show us that the force of <u>nature</u> is beyond our control.

waking [WAY king] *v.* stopping sleeping
   She plans on <u>waking</u> up at 5:30 A.M. in order to catch the early train.

winding [WYN ding] *adj.* curving or bending
   It was impossible to see anything beyond the bend of the <u>winding</u> road.

Word List B

complexion [kuhm PLEK shun] *n.* the natural color and appearance of the skin on one's face
   Like many redheads, Terry has a pale, freckled <u>complexion</u>.

eternal [ee TER nuhl] *adj.* continuing forever
   The young couple believed their love was <u>eternal</u>, but then they broke up.

loneliness [LOHN lee nis] *n.* the feeling of being alone and unhappy
   Will's <u>loneliness</u> ended when his best friend visited.

possession [poh ZE shun] *n.* the state of having or owning something
   It is against the law to have stolen property in your <u>possession</u>.

sonnet [SAH nit] *n.* a fourteen-line poem, with a set rhyme scheme
   The young poet wrote a <u>sonnet</u> for his beloved on Valentine's Day.

temperate [TEM puhr it] *adj.* mild, not extreme
   Because of her <u>temperate</u> personality, Jill never shouted or yelled.

Poetry Collection: Priest Jakuren, Ono Komachi, Theodore Roethke, William Shakespeare
Vocabulary Warm-up Exercises

Exercise A *Fill in each blank in the paragraph with an appropriate word from Word List A. Use each word only once.*

Kate enjoyed studying biology, and she especially enjoyed field trips out in

[1] _____. One morning, she remembered upon [2] _____

up that she had a field trip that afternoon. Her biology teacher was taking the class to a

nearby forest, where a [3] _____ trail curved through the pine trees.

Although they had planned to watch birds, their teacher insisted that they also stop to

study the [4] _____ caterpillars that crawled along in the undergrowth.

She wanted the class to [5] _____ the colors and sizes of the various types

of caterpillars. Although Kate had never been interested in caterpillars before, she was

soon fascinated. She felt that her entire [6] _____ was fulfilled by this kind

of work, and she made up her mind to pursue a career in science.

Exercise B *Write a complete sentence to answer each question. For each item, use a word from Word List B to replace each underlined word or words without changing the meaning.*

Example: Do you have a favorite <u>poem</u> by Shakespeare?
My favorite <u>sonnet</u> by Shakespeare is "Sonnet 116."

1. Do you have a <u>mild</u> reaction when experiencing anger and jealousy?

   _____

2. Does your <u>facial skin</u> show any signs of wrinkles?

   _____

3. Are any important belongings in your <u>custody</u>?

   _____

4. Do you feel that there are some values that are <u>everlasting</u>?

   _____

5. Have you ever felt <u>sadness</u> when you are by yourself?

   _____

Name _____   Date _____

Poetry Collection: Priest Jakuren, Ono Komachi, Theodore Roethke, William Shakespeare
Reading Warm-up A

Read the following passage. Pay special attention to the underlined words. Then, read it again, and complete the activities. Use a separate sheet of paper for your written answers.

Andy was dreaming that he was stuck on a gigantic glacier with no hope of rescue and no food to eat. When he found himself <u>waking</u> up early that mid-October morning, he realized why. It was chilly in his tent, and he was hungry after all of yesterday's hiking.

Andy and his friends Kyle and Dennis had decided to go out into <u>nature</u> on a great adventure. They planned to hike the trails up the mountain outside of town. On their first day, they hiked for miles on a narrow, <u>winding</u> trail, resting only when they felt like they could go no farther. It was hard to <u>compare</u> this hike to earlier ones because this was the first time they had tried to cover so much ground. Also, on their other hikes, they had not carried camping gear. This trip was supposed to last three days. They knew they should not wear themselves out on the first day, but they were so eager to reach the mountain-top that they overextended themselves.

After a quick meal of peanut butter sandwiches and nutrition bars, the boys had gone to sleep. That is when Andy felt the cold in his dreams. He shivered in his sleep, imagining that he was frozen right into the glacier. The chill seemed to creep through his whole <u>being</u>, from the top of his head to the soles of his feet.

What a nightmare! Andy felt enormous relief when he woke up. He was grateful to be the first one up so that he could enjoy the sunrise in solitude. Though he did not like to wax poetic to his friends, he loved nature and especially loved spending time outdoors alone. He observed everything from the <u>lowly</u> ant to the soaring eagle, and he was mesmerized by all of it.

Then Kyle and Dennis woke up and the three were soon, back on their trail of adventure.

1. Circle the words that tell when Andy was <u>waking</u> from sleep. Write an antonym for *waking*.

2. Underline the phrase that tells where in <u>nature</u> Andy and his friends planned to hike. Then, tell what *nature* is.

3. Circle the word described by the adjective <u>winding</u>. Then, tell what *winding* means.

4. Underline the phrase that tells what made this hike hard to <u>compare</u> to earlier ones. Then, explain what *compare* means.

5. Underline the expression that describes how Andy felt the chill through his whole <u>being</u>. Then, use *being* in a sentence.

6. Circle the word that tells what <u>lowly</u> animal Andy observed. Describe what *lowly* means.

Poetry Collection: Priest Jakuren, Ono Komachi, Theodore Roethke, William Shakespeare

Reading Warm-up B

Read the following passage. Pay special attention to the underlined words. Then, read it again, and complete the activities. Use a separate sheet of paper for your written answers.

The sonnets of William Shakespeare are among the best-loved poems in the English language. In these fourteen-line poems, Shakespeare explores the <u>eternal</u> themes of love, death, and immortality.

Some of the sonnets are addressed to a handsome young man, possibly a nobleman. In some poems, the narrator encourages the "Fair Youth" to marry and produce children who will inherit his good looks. Indeed, in "<u>Sonnet</u> 3," the narrator ends by warning, "Die single and thine image dies with thee." The narrator of the poems seems to feel great affection for this young man, and expresses sorrow and <u>loneliness</u> when he and his friend are apart.

Other poems are addressed to a woman who has come to be known as Shakespeare's "Dark Lady." Scholars call her the Dark Lady for many reasons. In some of the sonnets, for example, Shakespeare describes her <u>complexion</u> as being black. In others, Shakespeare describes his lady's hair and eyes as being dark. Also, darkness is associated with both mystery and excess. In some of the sonnets to the Dark Lady, Shakespeare implies that she is dishonest. A number of sonnets express both love and hatred for this woman. The narrator's emotions are neither <u>temperate</u> nor tame, especially when the Dark Lady is unfaithful, as exemplified in "Sonnet 147": "For I have sworn thee fair, and thought thee bright, Who art as black as hell, as dark as night."

Scholars have long tried to determine the identities of the Fair Youth and the Dark Lady. Of course, that assumes that in these sonnets Shakespeare himself, speaking as the narrator, wrote these poems to actual people in his own life. None of this is certain. For hundreds of years, scholars have not been in <u>possession</u> of adequate information to determine just who these mysterious figures were or, indeed if they existed at all. Luckily, the sonnets transcend biographical details. They contain some of the most beautiful expressions of love in all of literature.

1. Underline the themes described as <u>eternal</u>. Write a sentence about literary themes that you believe are *eternal*.

2. Underline the phrase excerpted from Shakespeare's "<u>Sonnet</u> 3." Then, tell what a *sonnet* is.

3. Write a synonym for <u>loneliness</u>. Then, write about a time when you experienced *loneliness*.

4. Circle the word that describes the Dark Lady's <u>complexion</u>. Write a sentence about your own *complexion*.

5. Circle the word that means close to the same thing as <u>temperate</u>. Use *temperate* in a sentence.

6. Underline the words that tell what Shakespearean scholars are not in <u>possession</u> of. Explain why you think this might be so.

Name _____ Date _____

Poetry Collection: Priest Jakuren, Ono Komachi, Theodore Roethke, and William Shakespeare

Literary Analysis: Poetic Form

To unify sounds and ideas in a poem, a poet may follow a **poetic form,** or structure, using a set number of lines. Some have a unique **meter,** or rhythm, and a unique pattern of **rhymes.**

Elements	Tanka	Sonnet	Villanelle
Number of lines	5 (may vary in translation, but must be brief)	14: three 4-line *quatrains* + a 2-line *couplet*	19: five 3-line stanzas + one 4-line stanza. Lines 1 and 3 repeat.
Number of syllables/ each line	lines 1, 3 = 5 syllables lines 2, 4, 5 = 7 syllables (may vary in translation)	usually ten syllables per line	Poets may follow different patterns.
Pattern of accents	no set pattern	5 unaccented and 5 accented syllables per line	Poets may follow different patterns.
Rhyme scheme	none	abba, cddc, efef, gg **OR** abab, cdcd, efef, gg	aba, aba, aba, aba, aba, aba
Characteristics	brief; focuses on one idea	ideas in quatrains can answer one another; couplet is a summary	repetition can create chanting effect or suggest intensity

Directions: *Answer the following questions about the poems in this collection.*

1. **A.** How do the translations of the two tanka depart from traditional tanka form?

   _____

   B. Why do you think the translator made these changes in the form?

   _____

2. Read aloud the first two stanzas of "The Waking." Then, answer the questions.

   A. How many lines are in each stanza? _____

   B. What is the rhyme scheme of the two stanzas? _____

   C. Which line is repeated? _____

   D. In what poetic form is the poem written? _____

3. Copy out the first four lines of Shakespeare's Sonnet 18 on a separate sheet of paper. Then, answer the questions.

   A. Above each unaccented syllable, draw a ˘. Above each accented syllable, draw a ´.

   B. How many accented and unaccented syllables did you find in each line?

   _____

   C. What is the rhyme scheme of the lines? _____

Poetry Collection: Priest Jakuren, Ono Komachi, Theodore Roethke,
and William Shakespeare

Reading: Preview a Poem to Read Fluently

When you **read fluently,** you read smoothly and with understanding. You place emphasis appropriately and pause where necessary. To increase your fluency when reading a poem, **preview** the work. Look over the text in advance:

- Use footnotes and other text aids to learn unfamiliar words.
- Determine where each sentence in the poem begins and ends. Pause only when the punctuation indicates you should.
- Form a rough idea of the topic and mood of the work. Read the poem with its mood in mind.

DIRECTIONS: *Answer the following questions about the poems in this collection.*

1. Preview the poem "One cannot ask loneliness. . . ." What two end marks do you see in the poem? _____

2. Preview the poem "Was it that I went to sleep. . . ." How can the end marks help you read the poem smoothly and with understanding?

   _____

   _____

3. Preview lines 1–6 of "The Waking" and answer the questions.

   A. How many end marks do these lines contain? _____

   B. How does the number of end marks influence how you should read the lines fluently?

   _____

   C. How do the pauses in lines 1–6 help convey the meaning and theme of the poem?

   _____

   _____

   _____

4. In order to read Shakespeare's Sonnet 18 fluently, why is it important to make sure you understand the meanings of the words *temperate* and *eternal* when you preview the poem?

   _____

   _____

   _____

Poetry Collection: Priest Jakuren, Ono Komachi, Theodore Roethke,
and William Shakespeare

Vocabulary Builder

Word List

fate	eternal	lowly	temperate

A. DIRECTIONS: *Write whether each statement is* true *or* false. *Explain why.*

_____ 1. Parents can tell their child's *fate* at birth.

_____

_____ 2. Winters in northern Canada are usually *temperate*.

_____

_____ 3. Getting an education is one way that people rise from a *lowly*
position.

_____

_____ 4. An *eternal* mystery is one that can be easily solved.

_____

B. DIRECTIONS: *Choose the best **antonym** for each word.*

1. lowly
   A. softly   B. sharply   C. lofty   D. heavy
2. temperate
   A. warm   B. cool   C. mild   D. extreme
3. eternal
   A. mortal   B. immortal   C. alive   D. endless

Poetry Collection: Priest Jakuren, Ono Komachi, Theodore Roethke,
and William Shakespeare

Support for Writing a Tanka

Before drafting your tanka, read the simple example below. Then, draft your own tanka on the blank lines, using only the number of syllables indicated for each line. In your poem, you might want to describe your response to a specific type of weather.

Subject: Lying in bed listening to a storm outside
Mood: Cozy, thankful

Rain beats the windows.	**5 syllables**
Wind howls and sneaks through the cracks.	**7 syllables**
I smile with content.	**5 syllables**
Their fury cannot touch me.	**7 syllables**
I am snug and warm in bed.	**7 syllables**

Subject of Your Poem: _____

Mood You Want to Convey: _____

5 syllables _____

7 syllables _____

5 syllables _____

7 syllables _____

7 syllables _____

Poetry Collection: Priest Jakuren, Ono Komachi, Theodore Roethke,
and William Shakespeare

Support for Extend Your Learning

Research and Technology

Use the lines below to gather information for a visual presentation on Elizabethan art.

Specific descriptions in Sonnet 18:

_____

Mood conveyed in Sonnet 18:

_____

Artworks That Could Illustrate Sonnet 18:

Image 1: Title: _____
How artwork relates to poem: _____
Description of artistic style: _____

_____

Image 2: Title: _____
How artwork relates to poem: _____
Description of artistic style: _____

_____

Listening and Speaking

Use the chart to take notes for a discussion as you listen to a recording of Sonnet 18.

Speed of reading	
Reader's tone of voice	
Words reader emphasizes	
Where reader pauses	
How reader expresses rhythm/rhyme	

Name _____ Date _____

Poetry Collection: Priest Jakuren, Ono Komachi, Theodore Roethke,
and William Shakespeare
Enrichment: Waking, Sleeping, Dreaming

Around A.D. 800, the Chinese poet Ono Komachi wrote a tanka pondering the mysterious connection between her waking experiences and her dream life. More than a thousand years later, the American poet Theodore Roethke wrote his poem "The Waking" about what it means to be truly awake to the experiences of life. Our mysterious daily cycle of waking, sleeping, and dreaming is one that has fascinated people since ancient times. It continues to spark debate among scientists and psychologists.

Scientists have studied the brain waves of sleeping people and can now describe in detail how the body changes during different stages of sleep. However, no one really knows for sure why we need to sleep and why we dream.

Scientists have learned that dreaming is more common during the REM—"rapid eye movement"—stage of sleep. REM sleep is closely connected to wakefulness because the body's organs are still relatively active, and the muscles are still capable of movement, unlike in deep sleep. If people are deprived of REM sleep for several days, their wakeful thinking becomes disturbed. When they are allowed to rest again, they spend more time than usual in REM sleep to make up for the lost time.

Recently, scientists have become interested in mental states in between sleeping and wakefulness. For example, in the period when people are just dozing off or just waking up, the brain makes electrical waves that are unlike those of either sleep or normal wakefulness. If awakened suddenly at this point, people report vivid, free-floating imagery. Inventors, scientists, writers, and artists have reported that some of their most creative ideas have come to them when they were in this state.

Another "in-between" state of great interest is the so-called "flow state." This condition occurs when people are deeply involved in something they enjoy, such as sports, games, music, reading, or puzzle-solving. In this state, people lose awareness of distractions in their surroundings. They experience deep concentration and feel a sense of satisfaction and control. Psychologists say that making time for such experiences can help people stay mentally balanced.

1. Which interests you more—the scientific discoveries about waking, sleeping, and dreaming, or the poets' reflections on these topics? Explain why, citing at least two specific details from the passage above or specific imagery from the poems by Komachi and Roethke.

   _____

   _____

   _____

2. Using three details from the scientific evidence described above, explain why a poet like Roethke might say he prefers to "take my waking slow."

   _____

   _____

   _____

Poetry Collections: Ki Tsurayuki, Minamoto no Toshiyori, James Weldon Johnson, Dylan Thomas; Priest Jakuren, Ono Komachi, Theodore Roethke, and William Shakespeare

Build Language Skills: Vocabulary

The Latin Suffix -al

The Latin suffix -al means "of, relating to, or characterized by." It is used to form adjectives and nouns. For example, *national* means "of the nation."

A. DIRECTIONS: *Select a word from the box and add the suffix -al to complete each sentence.*

logic	margin	organization	tradition

1. The teacher added _____ notes on the report to suggest possible revisions.
2. On World Cultures Day, many students performed _____ dances.
3. The new club will hold its first _____ meeting on Friday to elect officers.
4. Jana's test grade was a _____ result of her hard work.

Academic Vocabulary Practice

compensate	diverse	radical	significance	visual

B. DIRECTIONS: *Write sentences, following the directions below.*

1. Give two examples that show how *diverse* modern music is.

   _____

2. Describe a *radical* improvement you would like to make in today's cars.

   _____

3. Explain the *significance* of the Internet in your life.

   _____

4. Explain how people can sometimes *compensate* for poor vision or poor hearing.

   _____

5. Describe your reaction to the *visual* impact of the night sky.

   _____

Poetry Collections: Ki Tsurayuki, Minamoto no Toshiyori, James Weldon Johnson, Dylan Thomas; Priest Jakuren, Ono Komachi, Theodore Roethke, and William Shakespeare

Build Language Skills: Grammar

Direct Objects

A **direct object** is a noun or pronoun that receives the action of a verb. It answers the question *what* or *whom*. Not all action verbs take a direct object. Verbs such as *am, is, are, was,* and *were* are linking verbs. They never take a direct object.

Jen makes **scrapbooks.**
(Jen makes *what*?) (has a direct object)

She spoke to the class about them.
(has an action verb, but no direct object)

Making scrapbooks is her favorite hobby.
(has a linking verb, no direct object)

A. DIRECTIONS: *Underline each direct object in the following sentences. If the sentence does not have a direct object, write* no d.o. *on the line.*

_____ 1. Sean likes very old movies.

_____ 2. He rents DVDs of old comedies.

_____ 3. His favorites are the Marx Brothers.

_____ 4. Sometimes I go to the video store with him.

_____ 5. He invited me to his house to watch a movie yesterday.

B. DIRECTIONS: *Write a paragraph about the kind of books, movies, sports, or crafts that you enjoy. Underline each direct object that you use in your paragraph.*

_____

_____

_____

_____

_____

Poetry Collection by Priest Jakuren, Ono Komachi, Theodore Roethke, and William Shakespeare

Selection Test A

Critical Reading *Identify the letter of the choice that best answers the question.*

____ 1. Which of the following are characteristics of the tanka form?
   A. 14 lines and 5 accented syllables per line
   B. a rhyme scheme of *aba*
   C. 5 lines and a syllable count of 5, 7, 5, 7, 7
   D. a rhyme scheme of *abba, cddc, efef, gg*

____ 2. When previewing the following lines from "One cannot ask loneliness. . . ," how often should readers plan to pause?

   On the cypress-mountain,
   Autumn evening.

   A. once, after *mountain*
   B. once, after *evening*
   C. twice, after *mountain* and *evening*
   D. Do not pause at all.

____ 3. What does the speaker of "One cannot ask loneliness . . ." say about loneliness?
   A. No one knows how it starts.
   B. No one knows how it ends.
   C. No one knows how to cope with it.
   D. No one knows how to cure it.

____ 4. In "Was it that I went to sleep . . . ," whom has the speaker been dreaming about?
   A. her dead mother
   B. her sick sister
   C. the man she loves
   D. a person she fears

____ 5. How does the speaker of "Was it that I went to sleep . . ." feel after waking up?
   A. relieved
   B. disappointed
   C. afraid
   D. enthusiastic

____ 6. What poetic form are the repeating lines in "The Waking" characteristic of?

    A. tanka

    B. sonnet

    C. villanelle

    D. narrative

____ 7. What is the rhyme scheme of the following lines from "The Waking"?

        I wake to sleep, and take my waking slow.

        I feel my fate in what I cannot fear.

        I learn by going where I have to go.

    A. *aba*

    B. *abb*

    C. *aab*

    D. *abc*

____ 8. What message does "The Waking" convey about learning?

    A. We learn the most from reading good books.

    B. We learn the most from listening to our elders.

    C. We learn the most from watching little children.

    D. We learn the most from pondering our experiences.

____ 9. Which of the following are characteristics of the sonnet form?

    A. 14 lines, regular rhythm and rhyme

    B. 5 lines, strict syllable count

    C. 19 lines, six stanzas, no rhyme

    D. 16 lines, no pattern of rhythm or rhyme

____ 10. In Sonnet 18, to what does the speaker compare his beloved?

    A. a spring morning

    B. a summer day

    C. an autumn evening

    D. a winter night

____ 11. When previewing the following lines from Sonnet 18, how many sentences should readers plan to read fluently?

        So long as men can breathe, or eyes can see,

        So long lives this, and this gives life to thee.

    A. none

    B. one

    C. two

    D. four

____ **12.** According to the speaker of Sonnet 18, where will his beloved remain young and beautiful forever?

    A. in his memory of her

    B. in his dreams about her

    C. in his painting of her

    D. in his poem about her

Vocabulary and Grammar

____ **13.** When is the *fate* of a criminal decided?

    A. when the crime is committed

    B. when the criminal is arrested

    C. when the trial begins

    D. when the trial ends

____ **14.** What does the *significance* of an event refer to?

    A. its location   **C.** its importance

    B. its length   **D.** its different parts

____ **15.** Which sentence includes a direct object?

    A. I went to the grocery store.

    B. I bought some plants.

    C. The aisles were crowded.

    D. I ran to the counter.

Essay

16. Which poem in this group did you find most unusual? In a brief essay, describe how the poem's subject matter and form contributed to your appreciation. In addition to telling what the poem is about, discuss its length and its stanzas (if any), any memorable images it includes, and any pattern of rhythm and rhyme that you enjoyed.

17. Both "Was it that I went to sleep . . ." and "The Waking" describe the process of waking up and the connections between being asleep and being awake. Which poem captured these experiences more vividly for you? In a brief essay, explain your choice. Give two reasons why the poet's description of waking and sleeping seem vivid and true-to-life.

Poetry Collection by Priest Jakuren, Ono Komachi, Theodore Roethke,
and William Shakespeare
Selection Test B

Critical Reading *Identify the letter of the choice that best answers the question.*

____ 1. What characteristic defines the tanka form?
A. its length and imagery
B. its rhythm and rhyme
C. its rhythm and imagery
D. its length and rhyme

____ 2. Which of the following does a tanka usually include?
A. a long description of natural events
B. a long description of the speaker's feelings
C. one line that tells the poem's meaning
D. one image that suggests the speaker's feelings

____ 3. In "One cannot ask loneliness. . .," what image captures the feeling of loneliness?
A. a barren seaside in winter
B. a cypress mountain in autumn
C. an empty lakeside in spring
D. a starless sky in summer

____ 4. When previewing the following lines from "Was it that I went to sleep. . .,"what should readers notice?
Was it that I went to sleep / Thinking of him, / That he came in my dreams?

A. The lines make one statement.
B. The lines ask one question.
C. The lines ask two questions.
D. The lines are not a complete sentence.

____ 5. What is the wish of the speaker of "Was it that I went to sleep. . ."?
A. She wishes she could stop dreaming.
B. She wishes she could wake up easily.
C. She wishes she were still dreaming.
D. She wishes she were not in love.

____ 6. Which of the following lines is repeated in "The Waking"?
A. I feel my fate in what I cannot fear.
B. I learn by going where I have to go.
C. I hear my being dance from ear to ear.
D. What falls away is always. And is near.

____ 7. Which sentence best expresses the message of "The Waking"?
A. Life is a journey that is lived one step at a time.
B. Life is a dream that has no reality whatsover.
C. The only way to experience joy is to awaken early.
D. The only escape from the pain of life is in dreams.

____ 8. Which characteristics make "The Waking" a good example of the villanelle form?
A. 14 lines, 5 accented syllables, rhyme scheme
B. 14 lines, 5 syllables per line, repeated lines
C. 19 lines, 6 stanzas, repeated lines
D. 19 lines, quatrains, rhyme scheme

____ 9. When previewing "The Waking," what should readers notice?
A. Each stanza is one complete sentence.
B. Most lines have at least one sentence.
C. There are no questions in the poem.
D. There are very few pauses in the poem.

____ 10. What is the rhyme scheme of "The Waking"?
A. abba, cddc, efef, gg
B. abab, cdcd, efef, gg
C. aba, aba, aba, aba, aba, abaa
D. abb, abb, abb, abb, abb, abba

____ 11. Even without its title, how could you tell that Sonnet 18 is a sonnet?
A. It has 14 lines and 5 unaccented and accented words per line.
B. It has 14 lines, 5 accented syllables per line, and no rhyme.
C. It has 19 lines, six stanzas, and a rhyme scheme.
D. It has 19 lines, along with lines and rhymes that repeat.

____ 12. Which characteristic of a sonnet is evident in the following lines from Sonnet 18?
Sometime too hot the eye of heaven shines,
And often is his gold complexion dimmed;
A. couplet
B. rhyme scheme
C. accent pattern
D. repetition

____ 13. When previewing Sonnet 18, what might readers notice?
A. It is about the many beauties of summer.
B. It is about the death of a beautiful woman.
C. It is about the poet's pride in his beloved.
D. It is about the heartbreak of lost love.

____ 14. According to Sonnet 18, what is one way to defeat death?
A. Be in tune with the changing cycles of nature.
B. Believe in the power of true love to last forever.
C. Immortalize your beloved in a work of literature.
D. Have children who will carry your dreams forward.

____ 15. What is a correct generalization about the three poetic forms in this group?
A. The tanka emphasizes rhyme more than the sonnet and the villanelle.
B. The sonnet and the villanelle emphasize rhyme more than the tanka.
C. The tanka emphasizes length more than the sonnet and the villanelle.
D. The sonnet and the villanelle emphasize imagery more than the tanka.

Vocabulary and Grammar

____ 16. When the speaker of "The Waking" says "I feel my *fate*," what does he mean?
   A. He analyzes his feelings.
   B. He anticipates his failure.
   C. He remembers his past.
   D. He senses his destiny.

____ 17. In the following lines from Sonnet 18, what does the word *temperate* mean?

   Shall I compare thee to a summer's day?
   Thou art more lovely and more *temperate*;

   A. wild and exciting
   B. mild and moderate
   C. tender and lovable
   D. changing and unreliable

____ 18. What is another way to describe *diverse* interpretations of a poem?
   A. They are different interpretations.
   B. They are similar interpretations.
   C. They are correct interpretations.
   D. They are incorrect interpretations.

____ 19. Which sentence does NOT include a direct object?
   A. We saw interesting exhibits at the museum.
   B. A guide told us facts about the artwork.
   C. We are planning another visit soon.
   D. I want to go again with my friends.

Essay

20. A tanka suggests deep feelings in a few brief lines. Sonnets and villanelles, on the other hand, include many lines and details to elaborate on a feeling. Which of the three forms do you think creates the most powerful, lasting effect on readers? Choose the poem in this group that had the strongest emotional impact on you. In a brief essay, describe its impact and explain how the poem's form and content help create that effect.

21. "The Waking" can be read as a description of waking up to face each new day. It can also be read as advice about how to live a good life. Choose one of the following lines from the poem's first stanza: "I wake to sleep and take my waking slow. / I feel my fate in what I cannot fear. / I learn by going where I have to go."

   In a brief essay, interpret the advice offered by the line you selected. Then, evaluate the advice. Give at least two examples from real life to show why the advice is wise or unwise.

22. What argument does the speaker develop in Sonnet 18? Write a brief essay to answer this question. In your essay, address the following questions: In the first quatrain, to what does the speaker compare his beloved? Why is his beloved superior? In the second quatrain, why is the line "And every fair from fair sometimes declines" important? In the third quatrain, how long does the speaker say his beloved's perfection will last? How does the point made in the couplet relate to the third quatrain?

Vocabulary Warm-up Word Lists

Study these words from the poetry of Mistral, Brooks, and Keats. Then, apply your knowledge to the activities that follow.

Word List A

casual [KA zhoo uhl] *adj.* relaxed and not worried about things
   You cannot go off for a <u>casual</u> stroll when the forecast calls for a blizzard.

haggard [HAG uhrd] *adj.* looking sick, tired, or worried
   We worried about our grandmother looking so tired and <u>haggard</u>.

horrid [HAWR id] *adj.* extremely bad or difficult
   Ms. Gulch had a <u>horrid</u> little dog that always tried to bite me.

meadow [MED oh] *n.* a field with wild grass and flowers
   The beautiful green <u>meadow</u> was dotted with yellow buttercups.

receipts [ri SEETS] *n.* pieces of paper showing that you have received money or goods
   You need to bring the <u>receipts</u> if you are returning those items to the store.

withered [WI<u>TH</u> uhrd] *v.* shriveled; dried up
   The bouquet <u>withered</u> after a week, so I discarded it.

Word List B

anguish [ANG gwish] *n.* suffering caused by extreme pain or worry
   The soldier's family felt terrible <u>anguish</u> when they heard news of the war.

loitering [LOY tuhr ing] *v.* standing in a public place without having a clear reason to be there
   Municipal laws often prohibit <u>loitering</u> in shopping or business districts.

sojourn [SOH jurn] *v.* to make a trip to stay somewhere
   We will <u>sojourn</u> to the mountains for our annual backpacking trip.

thrall [THRAWL] *n.* state of being controlled by someone or something
   Isabel was held in such <u>thrall</u> by her beau that she ate steak despite being a vegetarian.

warriors [WAWR ee uhrz] *n.* soldiers, especially skillful ones
   Only the most skilled <u>warriors</u> could join the ranks of the elite military unit.

woebegone [WOH bi gahn] *adj.* looking very sad
   The lost child looked <u>woebegone</u> as she stood weeping on the busy corner.

Poetry by Gabriela Mistral, Gwendolyn Brooks, and John Keats
Vocabulary Warm-up Exercises

Exercise A *Fill in each blank in the paragraph with an appropriate word from Word List A. Use each word only once.*

We decided to enjoy a family picnic on the fresh new grass out on the
[1] _____. The occasion was so [2] _____ that a blanket
spread on the ground served as our table. We were pleased to have assembled such a
delicious picnic from items quickly grabbed at the corner deli. The price was reasonable,
too, as shown on the [3] _____ that had been stuck into the picnic basket
along with the food. Before we headed off to pick our spring bouquets, I noticed my aunt
looking a little [4] _____. She said she was still recovering from a
[5] _____ case of influenza and would stay behind and rest. We picked a
special bouquet for my aunt, but the flowers [6] _____ quickly in the
warm sunshine.

Exercise B *Revise each sentence so that the underlined vocabulary word is used in a logical way. Be sure to keep the vocabulary word in your revision.*

Example: When my friend arrived safely, I felt great <u>anguish</u>.
When my friend did not turn up, I felt great <u>anguish</u>.

1. The young men <u>loitering</u> in the park walked briskly around the pond.
   _____

2. We always <u>sojourn</u> at the lake cabin, so we will not spend any time there as usual.
   _____

3. It was a peaceful, non-violent group, so membership was limited to <u>warriors</u>.
   _____

4. The teenager was <u>woebegone</u> when the boy she liked asked her to the party.
   _____

5. Danny was in <u>thrall</u> to his coach, so he never listened to him.
   _____

Name _____   Date _____

Poetry by Gabriela Mistral, Gwendolyn Brooks, and John Keats
Reading Warm-up A

Read the following passage. Pay special attention to the underlined words. Then, read it again, and complete the activities. Use a separate sheet of paper for your written answers.

Deborah loved to visit her elderly grandparents. They were her mother's parents, and they told her wonderful stories of what her mother was like when she was Deborah's age. They lived near a beautiful meadow, and Deborah loved wandering there in the spring when the flowers were beginning to bloom, and in the winter, after the flowers had withered and were dusted with the first snowfall. Her grandparents never seemed bothered by the way she talked and acted. Life seemed more casual and comfortable with them.

When Deborah went to visit her grandparents this year, she noticed that something had changed. Her grandfather looked tired and haggard. Grandma said that he was sick and worried about his medical bills. Deborah hated to see Grandpa sitting at the kitchen table, fingering his medical receipts as if trying to bring back the money he had already spent. The only good news was that the doctors seemed to think that his illness was curable, though it would take many expensive treatments.

The idea that Grandpa would not undergo the treatments because of money was too horrid to contemplate. Deborah remembered all that he had done for his community. He had been a leader in the Civil Rights movement, inspiring other African Americans to stand up for their rights, and he had helped to build a soup kitchen that served scores of people every day. He had always been there when others needed him. Who could come to his rescue now?

Deborah decided that she had to do something. She told her parents what was happening. They worked with her to publicize Grandpa's situation, and the community came through. Within a few weeks, Grandpa had all the money he would need, though he hated to take charity. Still, everyone remembered what he had done for them, and they were glad to do something in return.

1. Underline the word that tells what grew in the meadow. Then, explain what a *meadow* is.

2. Circle the words that tell when the flowers withered. Then, explain what *withered* means.

3. Circle the word that means close to the same thing as casual. Then, use *casual* in a sentence.

4. Underline the phrase that tells why Grandpa looked haggard. Then, use *haggard* in a sentence.

5. Circle the word that tells what receipts Grandpa was fingering. Explain what *receipts* are.

6. Underline the phrase that tells what idea was too horrid to contemplate. Then, tell what *horrid* means.

Poetry by Gabriela Mistral, Gwendolyn Brooks, and John Keats
Reading Warm-up B

Read the following passage. Pay special attention to the underlined words. Then, read it again, and complete the activities. Use a separate sheet of paper for your written answers.

In "La Belle Dame sans Merci," Keats presents a hero who feels great <u>anguish</u> when deserted by the woman he loves. This poem, using the form of a ballad, is inspired by the medieval notion of courtly love. In the Middle Ages, knights like Keats's hero were encouraged to choose women to fall in love with and to romanticize. In old tales of chivalry, the knight might become ill from the horrible sadness of unrequited love. He might be found <u>loitering</u> outside the noblewoman's home seeking merely a glimpse of his beloved.

During the Middle Ages, books were written on how to conduct courtly love. The lady would need to be at least as socially acceptable as the knight to be a suitable object of his love. The knight would at first be silently in <u>thrall</u> to the lady. Then, he would confess his feelings after months of suffering. Before the lady could consider returning the knight's feelings, he had to prove himself through heroic feats. Knights in love were encouraged to become daring <u>warriors</u>, doing battle in their lady's name. They might <u>sojourn</u> to a faraway land to seek a legendary prize. If, after silent suffering and heroic deeds, the lady was still not interested, the knight would be desolate.

In the literature inspired by notions of courtly love, often a <u>woebegone</u> man finds the object of his affection both wondrous and cruel. Because the knight was in the service of his beloved, he might chafe at his servitude. Indeed, many sonnets use the theme of courtly love praising a woman's beauty while, at the same time, berating her for not loving enough (or at all) in return. Still, writers often portrayed the love as a worthwhile end in itself. This love, they implied, transformed the hero in what approached a spiritual experience.

1. Underline the phrase that explains why Keats's hero feels great <u>anguish</u>. Then, tell what *anguish* is.

2. Have you ever seen people <u>loitering</u> in your town? Write a sentence about it.

3. Explain how a knight silently in <u>thrall</u> to a lady might behave.

4. Underline the phrase that tells what daring <u>warriors</u> would do. Then, use *warriors* in a sentence.

5. Use your own words to rewrite the sentence that contains the word <u>sojourn</u>.

6. Write a synonym for <u>woebegone</u>. Then, write a sentence about a time when you felt or looked *woebegone*.

Name _____ Date _____

Poetry by Gabriela Mistral, Gwendolyn Brooks, and John Keats
Literary Analysis: Tone and Mood

Tone is the author's attitude toward the reader or toward the subject of the work. It can be described with adjectives such as *formal* or *informal, playful* or *serious*. For example, the tone of "Fear" could be described as *serious* or *anxious*.

Mood, or atmosphere, is a general, unified feeling conveyed by the various details of a literary work. The mood of a work may be described with adjectives such as *joyous* or *gloomy, harsh* or *cozy*. The mood of "La Belle Dame sans Merci," for example, might be described as *dreamy*.

Writers establish tone and mood through word choice, details, images, subject matter, and setting. A poem set by a fireside on a snowy evening, for example, will have a very different feeling from a poem set in a bus station on a cold, rainy night.

DIRECTIONS: *Answer the following questions to help you analyze the tone and mood of "Fear," "The Bean Eaters," and "La Belle Dame sans Merci."*

1. A. What particular fear is explored in "Fear"? _____

    B. What details or images help convey this fearful mood? _____

    _____

    _____

    C. What other, positive feeling is conveyed by the poem? _____

2. A. In "The Bean Eaters," the characters eat a simple meal. What are they doing as they eat?

    _____

    B. In line 10, what are the "twinklings and twinges" that the old couple feel? _____

    _____

    C. Would you say that the speaker's attitude toward the "old yellow pair" is critical or respectful? Why? _____

    _____

3. A. In what time and place is "La Belle Dame sans Merci" set? _____

    B. List three words or phrases used to describe the knight. _____

    _____

    C. What overall feeling do the poem's setting, characters, and events help create? _____

    _____

Name _____ Date _____

Poetry by Gabriela Mistral, Gwendolyn Brooks, and John Keats
Vocabulary Builder

Word List

| haggard | thrall | sojourn |

A. DIRECTIONS: *Complete each sentence with a word from the Word List.*

1. Every autumn, we leave the city to _____ in the countryside.
2. We soon find ourselves in the _____ of the beautiful autumn colors.
3. After a few restful days of vacation, we no longer appear _____.

B. DIRECTIONS: *Find a synonym for each word in the Word List. Use each synonym in a sentence that makes the meaning of the word clear.*

Example: Word: *annoy*
Synonym: *bother*
Sentence: Humming in study hall may <u>bother</u> the other students.

1. *haggard*

Synonym: _____

Sentence: _____

2. *thrall*

Synonym: _____

Sentence: _____

3. *sojourn*

Synonym: _____

Sentence: _____

C. DIRECTIONS: *On the line, write the letter of the word that is most nearly the* opposite *in meaning to the word in CAPITAL LETTERS.*

____ 1. HAGGARD:
    A. wrinkled   C. youthful
    B. fresh   D. bored

____ 2. THRALL:
    A. eagerness   C. confinement
    B. ferociousness   D. independence

Name _____ Date _____

Support for Writing to Compare Literary Works

Before you draft your essay analyzing how each poet generates mood, complete the following graphic organizer. Use another sheet of paper if necessary.

	"Fear"	**"The Bean Eaters"**	**"La Belle Dame sans Merci"**
Emotional state of . . .	the speaker:	the speaker: the couple:	the speaker: the knight:
Details or images related to these emotional states			
The "world" of each poem			
Poem's overall mood			

Now, use your notes to write an essay analyzing the ways in which each poet generates a certain mood.

Name _____ Date _____

Poetry by Gabriela Mistral, Gwendolyn Brooks, and John Keats
Selection Test A

Critical Reading *Identify the letter of the choice that best answers the question.*

_____ 1. In "Fear," what does the speaker fear?
A. fear itself
B. her child's happiness
C. swallows and queens
D. her child's independence

_____ 2. In "Fear," the speaker says, "I don't want them to make / my little girl a princess." Why does she not want her little girl to be a princess?
A. She knows that princesses are not truly free.
B. She does not want her daughter to be happy.
C. She does not want her daughter to ruin her shoes.
D. She knows that her daughter has other plans for her life.

_____ 3. A poem's words and details give clues about the author's attitude toward his or her subject. In "Fear," what is Mistral's attitude toward the mother's fears?
A. She thinks that the mother's fears are unnecessary.
B. She feels sorry for the child who is smothered by such fears.
C. She believes that the mother's fears are not normal.
D. She sees that the mother's fears spring from her deep love.

_____ 4. In "The Bean Eaters," why does Brooks choose beans as the couple's main food?
A. because beans are different colors
B. because beans are simple
C. because beans are worthless
D. because beans are unusual

_____ 5. Based on the following lines from "The Bean Eaters," what feeling does Brooks have toward her subjects?

Two who are Mostly Good.
Two who have lived their day,
But keep on putting on their clothes
And putting things away.

A. respect
B. annoyance
C. embarrassment
D. amusement

____ 6. In "The Bean Eaters," what is the couple doing as they eat?
   A. putting things away
   B. staring at each other
   C. remembering the past
   D. counting their possessions

____ 7. In "La Belle Dame sans Merci," what is the knight suffering from?
   A. old age
   B. loneliness
   C. hunger
   D. the cold

____ 8. Which word best describes the lady in "La Belle Dame sans Merci"?
   A. generous
   B. proud
   C. lonely
   D. mysterious

____ 9. In "La Belle Dame sans Merci," the knight has a dream about "pale kings and princes." In the dream, what do these characters do?
   A. warn the knight about the lady
   B. compete with the knight for the lady's love
   C. heal the knight's ailment
   D. convince the lady to leave the knight

____ 10. Which detail helps to establish the lonely, desolate mood of "La Belle Dame sans Merci"?
   A. The squirrel's granary is full
   B. Her hair was long
   C. she lulled me asleep
   D. no birds sing

____ 11. How are "Fear" and "La Belle Dame sans Merci" similar?
   A. They both take place in the "real" world.
   B. They both feature characters who have lost someone they love.
   C. They both capture the inner, emotional world of a character.
   D. They both express the idea that love should be avoided at all costs.

___ 12. An author often uses setting to help create a certain mood, or feeling. In which of these poems does setting play an important role?
A. "Fear" and "The Bean Eaters"
B. "The Bean Eaters" and "La Belle Dame sans Merci"
C. "Fear" and "La Belle Dame sans Merci"
D. all three of the poems

___ 13. Which word could be used to describe the tone of "Fear," "The Bean Eaters," and "La Belle Dame sans Merci"?
A. scolding
B. humorous
C. serious
D. angry

Vocabulary

___ 14. What does the word *haggard* mean in the following passage from "La Belle Dame sans Merci"?
   O what can ail thee, knight-at-arms, / So haggard and so woe-begone?
A. on edge
B. lonely
C. confused
D. tired looking

___ 15. If a book has you in its *thrall,* what is happening?
A. You cannot bring yourself to read it.
B. You are totally absorbed in it.
C. You completely disagree with it.
D. You have become a character in it.

Essay

16. Each of these three poems—"Fear," "The Bean Eaters," and "La Belle Dame sans Merci"—expresses a different idea about love. In your view, which poem paints the most positive picture of love? Which poem gives the most negative picture of love? Explain your opinions in a brief essay.

17. What attitude toward the main characters do the authors express in their poems? (Think of the mother in "Fear," the couple in "The Bean Eaters," and the knight in "La Belle Dame sans Merci.") Why do you think the authors chose to write about these characters? Answer these questions in a brief essay.

Poetry by Gabriela Mistral, Gwendolyn Brooks, and John Keats

Selection Test B

Critical Reading *Identify the letter of the choice that best completes the statement or answers the question.*

____ 1. Which of the following words describes the tone of "Fear"?
A. uncertain
B. ironic
C. anguished
D. sarcastic

____ 2. In the following passage from "Fear," what does the speaker mean by "them"?
I don't want them to make
my little girl a princess.
A. magicians
B. the king and queen
C. the world in general
D. other children

____ 3. The speaker of "Fear" does not want her daughter to be made a queen because
A. being queen is a difficult job.
B. her daughter is of humble origin.
C. she knows her daughter has other plans for her life.
D. she would no longer have access to her daughter.

____ 4. What kind of world does "Fear" explore?
A. an inner, emotional world
B. a fantasy world
C. a distant kingdom
D. the outer world of people and events

____ 5. "The Bean Eaters" takes place
A. in a rundown shack.
B. in a rented back room.
C. on a park bench.
D. in a supermarket.

____ 6. Which word best describes the tone of the following lines from "The Bean Eaters"?
Two who are Mostly Good.
Two who have lived their day,
But keep on putting on their clothes
And putting things away.
A. critical
B. sorrowful
C. amused
D. respectful

Name _____ Date _____

____ 7. In "The Bean Eaters," what does Brooks mean when she writes that the couple remembers "with twinklings and twinges"?
A. that they remember both the good times and the bad times
B. that they remember to put things away, even if they do not want to
C. that they remember the past, but are more concerned with the pains of old age
D. that the beads and other objects in the room shine brightly as they reminisce

____ 8. In "The Bean Eaters," what quality of the couple's life does Brooks most want to convey?
A. its clutteredness
B. its absurdity
C. its simplicity
D. its extravagance

____ 9. In "La Belle Dame sans Merci," the outer world reflects
A. the lady's dark intentions.
B. the knight's emotional state.
C. the dangers of modern society.
D. the hopefulness of spring.

____ 10. Which of the following best describes the lady in "La Belle Dame sans Merci"?
A. generous and kind
B. proud and willful
C. cruel and unsympathetic
D. mysterious and enchanting

____ 11. What happens after the lady takes the knight to her cave?
A. The lady dances in the woods.
B. The knight makes the lady a garland.
C. The lady feeds the knight.
D. The knight falls asleep.

____ 12. In the end, "La Belle Dame sans Merci" is a poem about
A. hope and fulfillment.
B. love and loneliness.
C. despair and death.
D. courage and valor.

____ 13. What is the overall mood of "La Belle Dame sans Merci"?
A. dreamy
B. suspenseful
C. cheerful
D. menacing

____ 14. Which element helps to establish the mood of both "The Bean Eaters" and "La Belle Dame sans Merci"?
A. plot
B. setting
C. humor
D. speaker

____ 15. "Fear" and "La Belle Dame sans Merci" both explore the idea of
   A. wanting and getting.
   B. dreading the future.
   C. having and losing.
   D. falling in love.

____ 16. In literature, how is mood different from tone?
   A. Mood is the work's overall feeling, while tone is the author's attitude.
   B. Mood is the feeling of a particular detail, while tone is the work's overall feeling.
   C. Mood is limited to a particular character or speaker, while tone is general.
   D. Mood is the way a reader feels after reading a work, while tone is the feeling of the work itself.

____ 17. The speaker in "Fear" and the couple in "The Bean Eaters" both
   A. value the simple pleasures in life.
   B. dread the day when all will be lost.
   C. secretly hope that their lives will change.
   D. take comfort only in possessing things.

____ 18. The authors of "Fear," "The Bean Eaters," and "La Belle Dame sans Merci" view their subjects with
   A. suspicion.
   B. amusement.
   C. disgust.
   D. sympathy.

Vocabulary

____ 19. What does the word *sojourn* mean in this passage from "La Belle Dame sans Merci"?
   And this is why I sojourn here, / Alone and palely loitering,
   A. recline   C. weep
   B. stay   D. stumble

____ 20. Which of the following would most likely make you *haggard*?
   A. wearing four layers of clothing   C. working all night on a project
   B. having a joke played on you   D. giving someone the perfect gift

Essay

21. Each of these three poems—"Fear," "The Bean Eaters," and "La Belle Dame sans Merci"—illustrates a certain kind of love and expresses a main idea about it. In an essay, identify the kind of love each poem illustrates. Then, explain what the poem says about that kind of love.

22. Imagine that you can overhear each poet speaking to his or her main characters. What might each poet be saying to the character or characters? How might he or she be speaking? Would he or she be giving advice, asking questions, paying compliments, passing judgment—or something else entirely? In an essay, explain what you think each poet would say, and why.

23. A poem's setting, characters, and details can all help establish the poem's mood. In an essay, identify the mood of "Fear" and "La Belle Dame sans Merci." Then, explain how each poem's setting, characters, and other details contribute to this mood. In your opinion, which poem's mood is more distinct? Why?

Name _____ Date _____

Description: Descriptive Essay

Prewriting: Choosing Your Topic

Use the chart below to write down the names of the people who stand out in your memory. Then, write a list of details that you associate with each person.

Relationship	Name	Details about the Person
Family member		
Friend		
Teacher/Coach		
Community member		
Other People		

Drafting: Shaping Your Writing

Use the graphic organizer below to convey a single main impression of your subject. Record the details that help build this impression.

Main idea sentence:

Details in body paragraph 1:

Details in body paragraph 2:

Details in body paragraph 3:

Details in conclusion:

Writing Workshop—Unit 4, Part 1
Descriptive Essay: Integrating Grammar Skills

Varying Sentence Patterns

The typical sentence pattern uses a subject followed by a verb. To add interest to your writing, vary your sentences by starting some of them with prepositional phrases.

Basic Subject—Verb Pattern: We often light a fire on cold December days.

Start with a Prepositional Phrase: *On cold December days*, we often light a fire.

A **prepositional phrase** consists of a preposition, its object, and any words that modify the object. The **preposition** is the word that connects a noun or a pronoun to the rest of the sentence. The noun or pronoun it connects is called the **object of the preposition.**

Study this chart of words that are often used as prepositions.

Preposition That Often Show Time Relationships	after, at, before, during, since, until
Prepositions That Often Show Spatial Relationships	above, across, around, atop, behind, below, beneath, beside, between, down, in, inside, into, near, off, on, onto, out, outside, over, through, under, up, within
Other Common Prepositions	about, except, for, from, like, of, with, without

Identifying Prepositional Phrases

A. DIRECTIONS: *For each sentence, underline a prepositional phrase that you might move to the start of the sentence.*

1. An old house stands around the corner.
2. A tall tree grows beside the house.
3. The tree has sheltered the old house for over fifty years.
4. The tree loses its leaves like clockwork nearly every October 12.

Varying Sentences with Prepositional Phrases

B. DIRECTIONS: *On the lines provided, revise this paragraph so that it alternates sentences that use basic subject-verb pattern with sentences that begin with prepositional phrases. Move prepositional phrases already there or create your own prepositional phrases.*

The school day ended at 3 P.M. The children then often played together. They enjoyed Columbus Park. Younger children liked the swings and slides. Teenagers played ball or jogged. Some even went boating.

_____

_____

_____

_____

_____

Name _____   Date _____

Unit 4: Poetry
Part 1 Benchmark Test 7

MULTIPLE CHOICE

Reading Skills

1. When you read a poem fluently, how do you read it?
   A. aloud, without any pauses
   B. silently, picturing the images
   C. smoothly and with understanding
   D. slowly, pausing at the end of each line

Read the selection from "Sowing" by Edward Thomas. Then, answer the questions that follow.

> It was a perfect day
> For sowing; just
> As sweet and dry was the ground
> As tobacco-dust.
>
> 5 I tasted deep the hour
> Between the far
> Owl's chuckling first soft cry
> And the first star.

2. When reading this poem, where should you make your first pause?
   A. after *day* in line 1
   B. after *sowing* in line 2
   C. after *just* in line 2
   D. after *dust* in line 4

3. If you were reading the poem aloud, which words should you emphasize in line 5?
   A. *I*, *tasted*, and *deep*
   B. *I*, *deep*, and *hour*
   C. *tasted*, *deep*, and *hour*
   D. *deep*, *the*, and *hour*

4. In stanza 2, which words should you read together as a single unit?
   A. Owl's chuckling first soft cry / And the first star
   B. the hour / Between the far
   C. Between the far / Owl's chuckling first soft cry
   D. I tasted deep the hour / Between the far

Read the selection from "Stars" by A. E. Housman. Then, answer the questions that follow.

> The toil of all that be
> Helps not the primal* fault;
> It rains into the sea,
> And still the sea is salt.

* **primal** (PRY-muhl) from earliest times

5. When reading this poem aloud, how long should you pause after *fault*?
   A. very slightly
   B. longer than a slight pause, but less than a full stop
   C. full stop
   D. do not pause at all

6. In reading the poem aloud, which words should you emphasize in the last line?
   A. *still*, *sea*, and *salt*
   B. *And*, *still*, and *salt*
   C. *sea*, *is*, and *salt*
   D. *still*, *the*, and *sea*

7. Which text aid can best help you prepare to read the poem?
   A. the poet's name
   B. the poet's birth and death dates
   C. the line numbers
   D. the pronunciation and meaning of *primal*

8. When you preview a research source, what should usually be your first step?
   A. skim the table of contents
   B. scan the table of contents
   C. skim the index
   D. scan the index

9. If you were previewing a physical geography text and read this introduction, what text structure would you conclude this source uses?

   Earth is divided into eight major geographical areas, or terrestrial biomes, based on climate and the types of plant life it supports. Near the Equator are the tropical rain forests and, just north and south of these, tropical savannas. Beyond these are the planet's large desert areas and occasional chaparral, with their somewhat different plant life. Farther north and south are the grasslands, or prairie, and the temperate deciduous forests, where the dominant trees lose their leaves in winter. Next in the northern hemisphere come the boreal forests, or taiga, with their coniferous trees. Then, in the far north, just below the polar ice cap, is the arctic tundra, where few plants can grow.

   A. chronological order
   B. spatial order
   C. order of importance
   D. comparison-and-contrast organization

Literary Analysis: Speaker and Poetic Forms

10. What is the main purpose of a narrative poem?
   A. to describe a setting
   B. to convey character
   C. to express feelings
   D. to tell a story

11. Which is the best description of the traditional form of a tanka?
   A. a three-line poem with lines of seven, five, and seven syllables
   B. a five-line poem with five syllables in the first and third lines and seven in the others
   C. a poem of five to nine lines in which each line has five syllables
   D. a seven-line poem in which lines of five syllables alternate with lines of seven syllables

12. Where did the tanka originate?
   A. China
   B. Japan
   C. Korea
   D. India

13. What is the term for the author's attitude toward the reader or subject of a work?
   A. point of view
   B. tone
   C. voice
   D. mood

14. Which statement is true of a villanelle?
   A. It has fourteen lines.
   B. It uses little repetition.
   C. All stanzas but one have three lines.
   D. Each stanza rhymes *aba*.

An ancient Rome auspex told fortunes based on the flight of birds. Read the selection from James Russell Lowell's "Auspex," and answer the questions.

> My heart, I cannot still it,
> Nest that had song-birds in it;
> And when the last shall go,
> The dreary days to fill it,
> 5 Instead of lark or linnet,
> Shall whirl dead leaves and snow.
>
> Had they been swallows only,
> Without the passion stronger
> That skyward longs and sings,—
> 10 Woe's me, I shall be lonely
> When I can feel no longer
> The impatience of their wings!

15. What form of poem is this?
    A. a lyric poem
    B. a narrative poem
    C. a sonnet
    D. a villanelle

16. Which is the likeliest identity of the speaker in the poem?
    A. a young man who has been disappointed in love
    B. an old man who can no longer hear the poet and his song
    C. an ancient Roman auspex, studying the flights of birds on a spring day
    D. the poet, who compares himself to an auspex and his feelings or poems to birds

17. What mood does the imagery in lines 4–6 help convey?
    A. a happy mood
    B. a sad mood
    C. a frightening mood
    D. an angry, bitter mood

18. What is the rhyme scheme of each stanza in the poem?
    A. aabaab
    B. abcbca
    C. abcabc
    D. abcdbc

Read Michael Drayton's "Since There's No Help." Then, answer the questions about it.

> Since there's no help, come let us kiss and part;
> Nay, I have done, you get no more of me,
> And I am glad, yea glad with all my heart
> That thus so cleanly I myself can free;
> 5 Shake hands forever, cancel all our vows,
> And when we meet at any time again,
> Be it not seen in either of our brows
> That we one jot of former love retain.
> Now at the last gasp of love's latest breath,
> 10 When, his pulse failing, passion speechless lies,
> When faith is kneeling by his bed of death,
> And innocence is closing up his eyes,
>   Now if thou wouldst, when all have given him over, on his life
>   From death to life thou mightst him yet recover.

19. What type of poem is this?
    A. a Shakespearean sonnet
    B. a sonnet, but not a Shakespearean sonnet
    C. a narrative poem
    D. a villanelle

20. Who is the speaker in this poem?
    A. someone who has been disappointed in love
    B. someone who is dying
    C. someone who loves a woman who is dying
    D. someone who is studying medicine

21. How does the final couplet relate to the preceding three quatrains?
    A. It sums them up by focusing on the end of the relationship.
    B. It emphasizes them by restating the same ideas in different words.
    C. It broadens them by suggesting that the poem applies to others besides the speaker.
    D. It contradicts them by offering one last chance.

22. Which of these lines in the poem is perfect iambic pentameter?
    A. line 3
    B. line 9
    C. line 10
    D. line 14

Vocabulary

23. What is the meaning of the suffix -ance or -ence?
    A. full of
    B. without
    C. the state of being
    D. the act or process of

24. Which sentence uses the italicized word correctly?
    A. Was it an accident, or did he do it *deliverance*?
    B. Bring us *deliverance* from our woes!
    C. The mail carrier brought today's *deliverance* at two o'clock.
    D. When will she *deliverance* the package?

25. Which sentence uses the italicized word correctly?
    A. She shook her head to indicate her *refusal*.
    B. Put the trash in the *refusal*.
    C. If you *refusal* to go today, we can go tomorrow.
    D. He is a very critical and *refusal* person.

Grammar: Direct Objects and Prepositions

26. How many prepositions does this sentence contain?

    On Saturday I went to meet Cindy for lunch at the mall and then we went to the movies.

    A. three
    B. four
    C. five
    D. six

27. Identify the prepositional phrase in this sentence:

    I am almost ready and will soon be leaving on my trip.

    A. almost ready
    B. will soon be
    C. leaving on my trip
    D. on my trip

28. What is the object of the preposition in this sentence?

    After the long wait, we were delighted to get a good seat.

    A. long
    B. wait
    C. get
    D. seat

29. Identify the direct object in this sentence:

    Mrs. Martinez is giving the class our weekly test today.

    A. class
    B. weekly
    C. test
    D. today

ESSAY

30. Write your own brief lyric poem in which the speaker is something nonhuman. For example, the speaker could be an object, such as a piano or a tree, or it could be an abstract idea, such as Love or Joy.

31. Write your own tanka. It could be about something in the natural world or something else in your everyday life. Remember to follow tanka form.

32. Think of a place that is special to you. It might be a place you visit all the time or one to which you go only occasionally. Then, write a brief essay describing the place, using sensory details and figurative language.

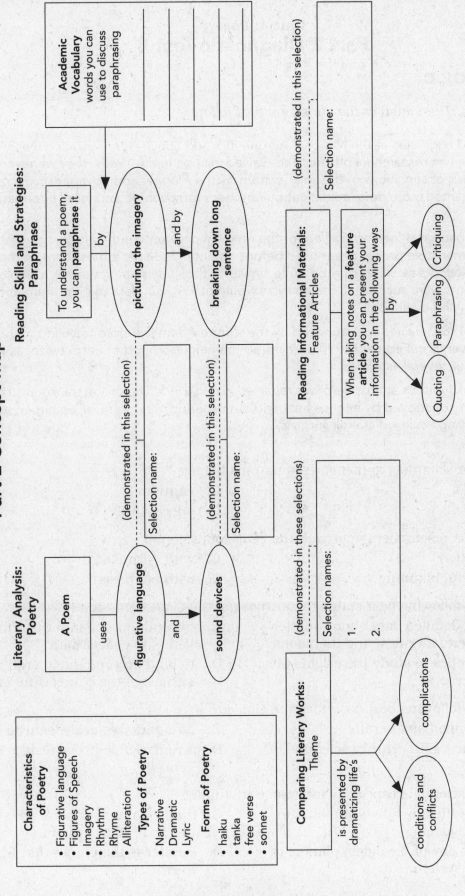

Unit 4: Poetry
Part 2 Concept Map

Academic Vocabulary words you can use to discuss paraphrasing

Reading Skills and Strategies: Paraphrase

To understand a poem, you can **paraphrase** it

by → **picturing the imagery**

and by → **breaking down long sentence**

(demonstrated in this selection)
Selection name:

(demonstrated in this selection)
Selection name:

Literary Analysis: Poetry

A Poem

uses → **figurative language**

and → **sound devices**

Characteristics of Poetry
- Figurative language
- Figures of Speech
- Imagery
- Rhythm
- Rhyme
- Alliteration

Types of Poetry
- Narrative
- Dramatic
- Lyric

Forms of Poetry
- haiku
- tanka
- free verse
- sonnet

Comparing Literary Works: Theme

is presented by dramatizing life's

→ complications

→ conditions and conflicts

(demonstrated in these selections)
Selection names:
1.
2.

Reading Informational Materials: Feature Articles

When taking notes on a **feature article**, you can present your information in the following ways

by →
- Quoting
- Paraphrasing
- Critiquing

(demonstrated in this selection)
Selection name:

Part 2 Student Log

Complete this chart to track your assignments.

Writing	Extend Your Learning	Writing Workshop	Other Assignments

Unit 4: Poetry
Part 2 Diagnostic Test 8

MULTIPLE CHOICE

Read the selection. Then answer the questions that follow.

The scientists and engineers at the National Aeronautics and Space Administration (NASA) are usually cautious, however, when researchers planned the *Galileo* mission in the 1980s, they were very bold. They thought that previous observations of the solar system by the *Pioneer* and *Voyager* spacecraft were incomplete. They wanted more detailed data about Jupiter's atmosphere and more information about its moons and rings.

The unmanned spacecraft, named *Galileo* for the renowned seventeenth-century scientist, was equipped with a remarkable probe, never used before, to enter Jupiter's atmosphere. In the scientists' opinion, the planet and its satellites may be quite similar to the early solar system as a whole. If *Galileo*'s numerous instruments were successful, the analysts would have much data to help them understand planetary formation and evolution.

On October 18, 1989, *Galileo* was launched by the shuttle Atlantis. Before traveling to Jupiter, the spacecraft flew by Venus in February 1990. It revisited the neighborhood of Earth twice, as well as recording data about several asteroids.

Galileo's probe of Jupiter's atmosphere was released in mid-1995. The probe transmitted data for only an hour before being destroyed by intense heat and atmospheric pressure. *Galileo* ended its primary mission in 1997, having achieved overall success.

1. How do NASA scientists and engineers usually behave?
   A. quickly
   B. boldly
   C. cautiously
   D. successfully

2. How did NASA researchers approach the *Galileo* mission?
   A. with caution
   B. with careful planning
   C. with enthusiasm
   D. with boldness

3. Which of the following best states the purpose of the *Galileo* mission?
   A. to collect detailed data about Jupiter's atmosphere, its rings, and its moons
   B. to use probes to study the origins of the universe
   C. to send a probe into the atmosphere of Venus to collect data
   D. to land an unmanned craft on the surface of the planet Jupiter

4. Which of the following best describes the *Galileo*?
   A. an unmanned spacecraft
   B. a renowned 17th century scientist
   C. a remarkable probe sent to study Mars
   D. a remarkable probe sent to study Venus

5. Why are the scientists especially interested in Jupiter?
   A. Jupiter is the most distant planet in the solar system.
   B. Jupiter is one of the oldest planets in the solar system.
   C. Jupiter and its moons are similar to the early solar system.
   D. Jupiter is the planet that is most like Earth.

6. What heavenly bodies besides Jupiter does *Galileo* study?
   A. Venus and Mars
   B. Earth, Mars, and Mercury
   C. Venus, Earth, Earth's moon
   D. Venus and asteroids

7. What do scientists hope to learn from studying Jupiter?
   A. the distance between Jupiter and Earth
   B. how planets formed and evolved
   C. what the solar system is like
   D. why Jupiter has moons

8. How did the *Galileo* mission end?
   A. The probe was destroyed in by heat.
   B. The mission ended in 1997 in success.
   C. The probe failed to send usable data.
   D. The *Galileo* mission is ongoing.

Read the selection. Then answer the questions that follow.

The first time James glimpsed the night sky through a telescope, he was surprised and excited. All those specks of light suddenly became actual places—not specks, but planets, just like Earth. Through the telescope, James could see that the moon was not a smooth disk, but had features such as ridges and valleys, and he could even envision walking on the moon some day. It was 1955, however, and space travel had not yet been attempted. James had never been inside an airplane, and in fact, he'd never left the state of Iowa, but he believed that one day he would man a space ship and walk on other planets.

Every night he scanned the sky with his telescope. He learned to identify Mars, with its distinct red color, as if its surface were covered in desert. Jupiter was slightly yellow, while Venus was the brightest, but he was most fascinated with Saturn, with its beautiful rings.

By the time he had finished college, the government had launched a full-blown space program and needed people like James for a mission to the moon. James joined the Air Force and then applied to the astronaut training program at NASA. Remarkably, he was chosen and in 1969 became one of the first people to walk on the moon.

9. What surprised James the first time he looked through a telescope at the night sky?
   A. The planets seemed so close to Earth.
   B. The night sky was so beautiful.
   C. The little specks of light were planets.
   D. There were so many stars.

10. What did James see on the moon through the telescope?
    A. features such as ridges and valleys
    B. the moon's smooth, disk-like surface.
    C. the thin atmosphere
    D. the footprints of astronauts

11. Which of the following is the best reason why James's desire to walk on the moon seemed an unrealistic at the time?
    A. He had never flown in an airplane.
    B. Space travel had not yet occurred.
    C. He had never left Iowa.
    D. He was very young.

12. Which of the following best describes the planet Mars?
    A. the brightest planet in the sky
    B. having a distinct yellowish color
    C. having beautiful rings
    D. having a reddish, desert-like surface

13. Which of the following best shows James's interest in space travel?
  A. He studied the sky with a telescope.
  B. He traveled in an airplane.
  C. He went to college.
  D. He liked space objects.

14. How did James prepare himself for becoming an astronaut?
  A. He flew in an airplane.
  B. He joined the Air Force.
  C. He believed he could be an astronaut.
  D. He applied for astronaut training.

15. How did James realize his dream?
  A. He became an Air Force pilot and flew fighter planes.
  B. He studied about the planets that he had seen through his telescope.
  C. He became an astronaut and walked on the moon.
  D. He applied to the training program for astronauts at NASA.

Vocabulary Warm-up Word Lists

Study these words from the poetry of Komunyakaa, Merriam, and Dickinson. Then, apply your knowledge to the activities that follow.

Word List A

flitting [FLIT ing] *v.* moving quickly from one place to another
   The children were <u>flitting</u> around the playroom from one toy to another.

impossible [im PAHS uh buhl] *adj.* not able to be done or to happen
   It is <u>impossible</u> to foretell the future with 100 percent accuracy.

makeshift [MAYK shift] *adj.* temporary, provisional
   The <u>makeshift</u> construction would not withstand strong winds.

numerous [NOO mer us] *adj.* many
   There are <u>numerous</u> beaches along the California coast.

superior [soo PEER ee uhr] *adj.* better than other people or things
   I believe that Mozart's music is <u>superior</u> to Bach's.

survive [suhr VYV] *v.* to continue to live normally, despite difficulties
   I could not <u>survive</u> the loss of my dog without the help of my friends.

Word List B

conjured [KAHN juhrd] *v.* having performed tricks in which you seemed to make things appear, disappear, or change as if by magic
   The magician <u>conjured</u> a flock of doves onstage.

countenance [KOWN tuh nuhns] *n.* face
   Her <u>countenance</u> was lit up by a radiant smile.

metaphor [MET uh fawr] *n.* a way of describing something by comparing it to something else without using the words "like" or "as"
   The <u>metaphor</u> "She is a walking encyclopedia" rightly described the genius.

raconteur [rak uhn TOOR] *n.* a person who tells entertaining stories
   The <u>raconteur</u> amused us for hours with his stories.

residence [REZ i duhns] *n.* the place where one lives
   Her <u>residence</u> is that lovely home at 2050 Evergreen Lane.

tremulous [TREM yoo luhs] *adj.* wavering; quivering
   His voice was <u>tremulous</u> when he talked back to the school bully.

Poetry Collection: Yusef Komunyakaa, Eve Merriam, Emily Dickinson
Vocabulary Warm-up Exercises

Exercise A *Fill in each blank in the paragraph with an appropriate word from Word List A. Use each word only once.*

It is hard to imagine how we would ever [1] _____ the school year without our favorite teacher, Mrs. Daley. She seems to find a way to bring out [2] _____ qualities in every student. Even students who are otherwise [3] _____ from one interest to another are able to focus their full attention on Mrs. Daley's assignments. There is absolutely nothing improvised or [4] _____ about her well-prepared lessons. Her classes include smooth presentations, active discussions, and thought-provoking assignments. It is virtually [5] _____ to suggest improvements to Mrs. Daley's excellent teaching. It is no surprise, then, to learn that she has received [6] _____ awards for outstanding teaching.

Exercise B *Revise each sentence so that the underlined vocabulary word is used in a logical way. Be sure to keep the vocabulary word in your revision.*

Example: As usual, the <u>raconteur</u> was silent throughout the entire evening.
As usual, the <u>raconteur</u> kept us entertained throughout the entire evening.

1. She sang the final note strongly with her <u>tremulous</u> voice.

   _____

2. A <u>metaphor</u> compares two things using the word "like" or "as."

   _____

3. Consumers found the flimsy product <u>superior</u> to its more solid competition.

   _____

4. The new <u>residence</u> on Tenth Street is for businesses, so no one will live there.

   _____

5. When the magician <u>conjured</u> my own scarf, I yawned with boredom.

   _____

Name _____ Date _____

Poetry Collection: Yusef Komunyakaa, Eve Merriam, Emily Dickinson
Reading Warm-up A

Read the following passage. Pay special attention to the underlined words. Then, read it again, and complete the activities. Use a separate sheet of paper for your written answers.

One of the most popular forms of recreation for adult Americans is sports. While it is <u>impossible</u> for most Americans to make their living as athletes, many can enjoy playing sports as amateurs.

<u>Numerous</u> options are available to someone who is interested in becoming involved in sports. One can choose to take part in team sports. These include softball, soccer, basketball, and volleyball. In these sports, it is important to practice with your team so that you can work together effectively. Some adult leagues are <u>makeshift</u> at best, emphasizing fun instead of organization. Other leagues require a huge time commitment; they take the sport and the competition very seriously indeed. In these leagues, athletes are not simply <u>flitting</u> from one recreational activity to another. All are focused on playing at the top of their chosen sport.

One might also choose an individual sport, such as running, bicycling, or golf. With these sports, individuals can compete in races or tournaments. Alternately, one can compete against his or her own personal best. An individual sport such as jogging can easily become part of a person's weekly schedule. For that reason, some consider year-round individual sports <u>superior</u> to seasonal team sports in helping a person to maintain fitness and health.

A third option is recreational sports, such as fishing, hiking, or boating. These sports are wonderful for relaxation. They generally do not place as much emphasis on competition as other sports do.

According to the Sporting Goods Manufacturers Association, Americans are most enthusiastic about individual sports. Their top five sports are swimming, walking, bicycling, bowling, and fishing. Others on the top ten are lifting free weights, camping in tents, and day hiking. Team sports such as volleyball, soccer, and touch football are in the top thirty. Any one of these worthwhile sports can help individuals <u>survive</u> the tedium of the average workweek, and provide plenty of fun.

1. Underline the phrase that tells what is <u>impossible</u> for most Americans. Then, tell what *impossible* means.

2. Underline the sentence in which the word <u>numerous</u> appears. Rewrite the sentence using your own words.

3. Circle the words that tell what are <u>makeshift</u>. Explain what *makeshift* means.

4. Underline the sentence that tells what people are doing instead of <u>flitting</u> from one recreational activity to another. Then, tell what *flitting* means.

5. Underline the phrase that tells in what way year-round individual sports might be <u>superior</u> to seasonal team sports. Use *superior* in a sentence.

6. Underline the phrase that tells what sports can help individuals <u>survive</u>. Explain what *survive* means.

Poetry Collection: Yusef Komunyakaa, Eve Merriam, Emily Dickinson
Reading Warm-up B

Read the following passage. Pay special attention to the underlined words. Then, read it again, and complete the activities. Use a separate sheet of paper for your written answers.

A literary device that has existed since antiquity is the underline{metaphor}. A metaphor makes a comparison between two seemingly unrelated things—such as "my love is a rose" or "their residence is a hornet's nest." The rose calls to mind the beauty of the beloved; the hornet's nest calls to mind unpleasant noise and activity that takes place in the home.

Similes also compare two seemingly unrelated subjects, but they use the words "like" or "as" to make the analogy clear. For example, "My love is like a rose" or "Her countenance was as unwelcoming as a locked door" are similes. Writers and speakers use both similes and metaphors to create lively impressions.

Sometimes, a writer might extend a metaphor, highlighting the point he or she is trying to make. For example: "The baby was a raconteur, entertaining the whole family with his babbling." Equating the baby's babbling with a raconteur's storytelling emphasizes its entertainment value.

Less skillful writers sometimes use mixed metaphors. In these, an item is compared to another, but then the writer jumps to yet another comparison that is not consistent with the first. For example, "Bridget's speech was a tremulous song, and she hit it out of the ball park" is a mixed metaphor. Bridget's speech is first compared to quivering sounds of music, but it is then compared to a homerun. The images do not work together.

Some metaphors compare things that are entirely dissimilar. These are called absolute metaphors or anti-metaphors. For example, "The magician conjured a rabbit—the piano of the art of magic" is an absolute metaphor. How is a rabbit at all like a piano? The reader is left confused.

According to Aristotle, "The greatest thing by far is to be a master of metaphor. It is the one thing that cannot be learned from others; it is also a sign of genius, since a good metaphor implies an eye for resemblance."

1. Underline the sentence that defines what a metaphor is. Write an example of a *metaphor*.

2. What does the metaphor compare a residence to? Rewrite the metaphor using your own words.

3. Write a synonym for countenance. Then, describe an unwelcoming *countenance*.

4. What types of things might a raconteur share with listeners? Write a sentence about someone you had describe as a *raconteur*.

5. Circle the word that tremulous describes. Then, use *tremulous* in a sentence.

6. Circle the word that tells what the magician conjured. Write about something that a magician has *conjured* in front of your eyes.

Name _____ Date _____

Literary Analysis: Figurative Language

Figurative language is language that is not meant to be taken literally. Poets often use **figures of speech** to convey their ideas in fresh and innovative ways. Figurative language includes these devices:

- A **simile** is a comparison of unlike things using the words *like* or *as.*
- In a **metaphor,** one thing is spoken about as if it were something else.
- In **personification,** an object, animal, or idea is spoken of as if it were human.

Because figurative language is often used to express meaning in concrete pictures, it is an important source of **imagery,** or word-pictures, in poetry.

Read these lines from "The Wind—tapped like a tired Man."

He visited—still flitting— / Then like a timid Man / Again, He tapped—'twas flurriedly—

Notice the use of simile, where the poet uses *like* to compare the wind to a timid man. The poet also personifies the wind.

A. DIRECTIONS: *Complete the following chart by recording two examples of each type of figurative language from the poems.*

Simile		
Metaphor		
Personification		

B. DIRECTIONS: *On the following lines, use each form of figurative language to describe a flower of your choice.*

Flower: _____

Simile: _____

Metaphor: _____

Personification: _____

Name _____ Date _____

Reading: Picture Imagery to Paraphrase Poems

To understand a poem, **paraphrase** it, or restate the meaning of lines in your own words. Begin by **picturing the imagery,** forming clear pictures of the descriptive details in the poem. Then, consider how the lines you will paraphrase are connected with these pictures.

Look at these lines from "Metaphor."

Morning is / a new sheet of paper / for you to write on.

You might picture a "new sheet of paper"—completely blank and empty. This can help you paraphrase the line as, "Morning is the start of a new day, blank and empty for experience to fill."

DIRECTIONS: *In the following chart, describe the image that each quotation creates. Then, restate the line in your own words.*

Quotation	Image	Paraphrase
1. The Sunday afternoon heat / Flared like thin flowered skirts (Komunyakaa)		
2. The bright words and the dark words / are gone (Merriam)		
3. A Rapid—footless Guest— / To offer whom a Chair (Dickinson)		

Poetry Collection: Yusef Komunyakaa, Eve Merriam, and Emily Dickinson
Vocabulary Builder

Word List

countenance   tremulous

A. DIRECTIONS: *On the following lines, write three examples that illustrate each word. For instance, if the word were* ingenious, *you might write* an imaginative inventor, a car that runs on vegetable oil, *or* a solution to an impossible math problem.

1. tremulous

   Example 1: _____

   Example 2: _____

   Example 3: _____

2. countenance

   Example 1: _____

   Example 2: _____

   Example 3: _____

B. DIRECTIONS: *Create two different sentences for each of the following words.*

1. countenance

   _____

   _____

2. tremulous

   _____

   _____

C. DIRECTIONS: *Find the pair of words that best expresses a relationship similar to that expressed in the pair in capital letters. Circle the letter of your choice.*

1. COUNTENANCE: FACE
   A. heart: lungs   C. limb: leg
   B. wink: smile   D. mouth: eyes

2. TREMULOUS: STEADFAST
   A. anxious: worried   C. trembling: shaking
   B. nervous: calm   D. joyful: happy

Poetry Collection: Yusef Komunyakaa, Eve Merriam, and Emily Dickinson
Support for Writing a Critical Essay

Before you begin writing your critical essay, determine what criteria you will use to evaluate the poems. Fill in the following chart with criteria for evaluating the poems, your evaluation of the poems, and quotations that support your evaluation.

Criteria for Evaluation: _____

_____

	Evaluation	Quotations
"Glory"		
"Metaphor"		
"The Wind—tapped like a tired Man"		

Now, use your notes to write your critical essay explaining which of these poems you found most effective.

Name _____ Date _____

Poetry Collection: Yusef Komunyakaa, Eve Merriam, and Emily Dickinson
Support for Extend Your Learning

Listening and Speaking

Write notes for your group discussion in the following chart. Include your opinion about the claim that each new day is like a fresh sheet of paper, reasons for your opinion, and quotations or examples that support your reasons.

My Opinion: _____

Reasons	Examples

Research and Technology

Use the following flowchart to note the important events in Emily Dickinson's publication history. Be sure to write the events in chronological order.

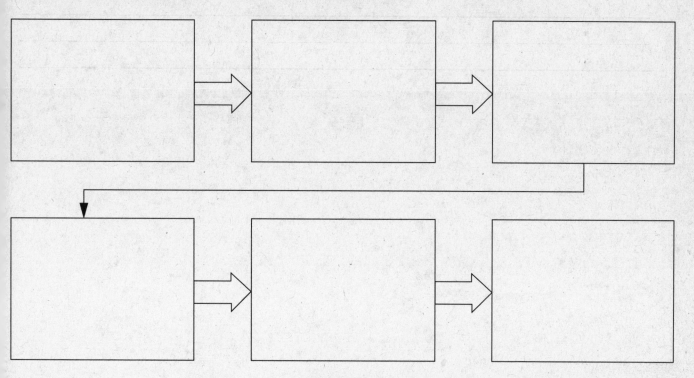

Name _____ Date _____

Poetry Collection: Yusef Komunyakaa, Eve Merriam, and Emily Dickinson

Enrichment: Baseball Greats

The poem "Glory" mentions four baseball greats: Jackie Robinson, Willie Mays, Josh Gibson, and Satchell Paige. All four were African Americans. Josh Gibson was a catcher in the Negro Baseball Leagues. Satchell Paige started out in the Negro Leagues and then became a Cleveland Indian. Jackie Robinson was the first African American to play in the major leagues; he played for the Brooklyn Dodgers. Willie Mays started out in the Negro Leagues and then played for the Giants. All four players are in the Baseball Hall of Fame.

DIRECTIONS: *Choose one of the four baseball players to research in a library or online. Find out what position the player played and how well he did. Write a brief biographical sketch of your subject on the following lines.*

_____

_____

_____

_____

_____

_____

_____

_____

_____

_____

_____

_____

Unit 4 Resources: Poetry
© Pearson Education, Inc., publishing as Pearson Prentice Hall. All rights reserved.
120

Name _____ Date _____

Poetry Collection: Yusef Komunyakaa, Eve Merriam, and Emily Dickinson
Selection Test A

Critical Reading *Identify the letter of the choice that best answers the question.*

____ 1. What are the "married teenagers" in "Glory" doing?
   A. working in an office
   B. playing baseball
   C. attending a concert
   D. singing and dancing

____ 2. What image do these lines from "Glory" create?
   The old deacons & raconteurs / Who umpired made an *Out* or *Safe* / Into a song & dance routine.
   A. deacons preaching at church
   B. a warm summer day
   C. old men singing and dancing
   D. ballplayers shouting "Out" and "Safe"

____ 3. Which of the following lines from "Glory" contains an example of a simile?
   A. Most were married teenagers
   B. They were all Jackie Robinson
   C. The men were like cats
   D. Runners hit the dirt

____ 4. What metaphor is central to the poem "Metaphor"?
   A. the comparison of bright words to dark words
   B. the comparison of morning to a blank sheet of paper
   C. the comparison of night to dawn
   D. the comparison of rest to wakefulness

____ 5. To the speaker of "Metaphor," what does each morning present?
   A. a chance for a fresh start
   B. more work
   C. time to deal with yesterday's problems
   D. more bright words than dark words

____ 6. Which of the following lines from "Metaphor" contains an example of personification?
   A. Morning is / a new sheet of paper
   B. until night / folds it up
   C. The bright words and the dark words
   D. a new day / to write on

_____ 7. What image does the following line from "Metaphor" create?

　　Morning is / a new sheet of paper

A. a page from a book

B. a blank piece of paper

C. a beautiful drawing

D. lines of writing

_____ 8. In "The Wind—tapped like a tired Man," who is the guest who enters the speaker's home?

A. a tired man

B. the wind

C. a musician

D. a hummingbird

_____ 9. What happens to the wind at the end of "The Wind—tapped like a tired Man"?

A. It leaves the house.

B. It blows very hard.

C. It knocks over glasses.

D. It cools down the house.

_____ 10. What word best describes the movement of the wind in "The Wind—tapped like a tired Man"?

A. vicious

B. clumsy

C. quick

D. steady

_____ 11. What image does the following line from "The Wind—tapped like a tired Man" create?

　　His Countenance—a Billow—

A. a strong gust of wind

B. curtains blowing inward

C. a bending tree

D. leaves blown through the air

_____ 12. How does the speaker seem to feel about the wind in "The Wind—tapped like a tired Man"?

A. She fears the wind.

B. She is confused by the wind.

C. She welcomes the wind.

D. She is angered by the wind.

Vocabulary and Grammar

____ **13.** Which of the following words has the same meaning as *tremulous*?
  A. proud   C. steady
  B. trembling   D. awed

____ **14.** Which word is a synonym for *minimize*?
  A. enrich   C. create
  B. reduce   D. analyze

____ **15.** Which words in the following sentence are a prepositional phrase?
      The umpires sing and dance as they call "safe" and "out" to the players.
  A. the umpires   C. sing and dance
  B. "safe" and "out"   D. to the players

Essay

16. In an essay, paraphrase the poem "Glory." Use your own words to tell what happens in the poem. Begin by forming clear pictures of the descriptive details in the poem. Then, consider how the lines you will paraphrase are connected with these pictures.

17. How is metaphor used in the poem "Metaphor" and in the poem "The Wind—tapped like a tired Man"? What comparisons are being made in the poems? How do these comparisons convey the themes of the poems? Answer these questions in an essay. Use details from the poems to support your ideas.

Poetry Collection: Yusef Komunyakaa, Eve Merriam, and Emily Dickinson
Selection Test B

Critical Reading *Identify the letter of the choice that best completes the statement or answers the question.*

____ 1. In "Glory," the "married teenagers" are men who are
  A. working in an office.
  B. umpiring the game.
  C. watching a ballgame.
  D. playing baseball.

____ 2. Which of these lines from "Glory" is an example of a simile?
  A. "Runners hit the dirt / & slid into homeplate"
  B. "A stolen base or homerun / Would help another man"
  C. "The Sunday afternoon heat / Flared like thin flowered skirts"
  D. "They were all Jackie Robinson / & Willie Mays"

____ 3. In "Glory," what is the "promise / Like a hesitation pitch" that the players feel?
  A. the promises great ballplayers make to always remember their fans
  B. the promises they make to win the game
  C. their hopes that a scout from a baseball team might be watching
  D. their dreams of a better life

____ 4. How would you best paraphrase these lines from "Glory"?
  The old deacons & raconteurs / Who umpired made an *Out* or *Safe* / Into a song & dance routine.

  A. The old deacons told stories about great *Outs* and *Safes.*
  B. Old raconteurs sang and danced on the field during the game.
  C. The umpires sang and danced when they made their calls.
  D. The umpires would rather sing and dance than do their jobs.

____ 5. What purpose does the game serve for the players in "Glory"?
  A. It enables them to face the work week.
  B. It gives them an outlet for their energy.
  C. It keeps them strong and healthy.
  D. It relieves the boredom of the weekend.

____ 6. How would you paraphrase the following lines from "Metaphor"?
  The bright words and the dark words / are gone / until dawn / and a new day / to write on.

  A. When morning arrives, you must face the problems of the previous day.
  B. You should always say and do what you want or else you will feel as though you failed at the end of the day.
  C. You can put the good and bad experiences of the day behind you and start fresh the next day.
  D. Some days will be filled with good experiences and some days will be filled with bad experiences.

_____ 7. The speaker in "Metaphor" sees each morning as
  A. a chance for a fresh start.
  B. time to face the weary work week.
  C. time to deal with yesterday's problems.
  D. more bright words than dark words.

_____ 8. In "Metaphor," the "bright words and the dark words" are a metaphor for
  A. daytime and nighttime.
  B. good experiences and bad experiences.
  C. words in black type and words in colored type.
  D. love and hate.

_____ 9. The guest whom the speaker invites into her home in "The Wind—tapped like a tired Man" is
  A. a ghostly being.
  B. the wind.
  C. a friend.
  D. a timid man.

_____ 10. In "The Wind—tapped like a tired Man," why does the poet compare the wind to "numerous Humming Birds"?
  A. to reveal the swiftness of the wind
  B. to show how beautiful the wind can be
  C. to illustrate the sound of the wind
  D. to reveal the wind's delicate nature

_____ 11. How would you describe the movement of the wind in "The Wind—tapped like a tired Man"?
  A. rapid and agitated
  B. delicate and silent
  C. vicious and intense
  D. slow and calm

_____ 12. How might you paraphrase the following stanza from "The Wind—tapped like a tired Man"?
  He visited—still flitting— / Then like a timid Man / Again, He tapped—'twas flurriedly—And I became alone—
  A. Wind darted around my home and then abruptly left.
  B. The wind gusted in my home. Then, it broke through the window.
  C. The wind became stronger and stronger until I had to seek cover.
  D. The wind stayed in my home until another visitor—a timid man—knocked on my door.

_____ 13. At the end of "The Wind—tapped like a tired Man," the speaker is
  A. left alone again.
  B. desperately longing for the wind.
  C. in a state of terror.
  D. filled with unexplained joy.

Vocabulary and Grammar

____ 14. Which of the following is the best meaning of the word *tremulous* as it is used in the following line from "The Wind—tapped like a tired Man"?

His fingers, as He passed / Let go a music—as of tunes / Blown tremulous in Glass—

    A. quiet   C. colorful
    B. trembling   D. agitated

____ 15. Which of the following words is a synonym for *countenance*?

    A. face   C. patience
    B. counter   D. wind

____ 16. A <u>drastic</u> change in someone is a change that is

    A. subtle.   C. ridiculous.
    B. unexpected.   D. extreme.

____ 17. Which of the following sentences contains a prepositional phrase?

    A. The ballplayers run the bases joyfully.
    B. The ballplayers only have Sundays off.
    C. The ballplayers' wives watch from the stands.
    D. The ballplayers do not care that it is hot.

____ 18. In which sentence is a prepositional phrase used as an adjective?

    A. The wind enters through the window.
    B. The wind makes a soft sound in the room.
    C. The wind moves around the room.
    D. The wind sounds like hummingbirds on a bush.

Essay

19. In a brief essay, identify how Dickinson uses figurative language to describe the wind in "The Wind—tapped like a tired Man." How would you describe the movement of the wind in the speaker's house? How does its visit affect the speaker, if at all? Cite examples from the poem to support your ideas.

20. Both "The Wind—tapped like a tired Man" and "Glory" describe an event. In your own words, tell what happens in the two poems. Refer to descriptive details from the poems as you paraphrase them in a brief essay.

Vocabulary Warm-up Word Lists

Study these words from the poetry of Millay, Ravikovitch, and Dickinson. Then, apply your knowledge to the activities that follow.

Word List A

gradually [GRA joo uhl lee] *adv.* little by little; slowly
   The clouds moved so <u>gradually</u> that they appeared to be standing still.

haste [HAYST] *n.* hurrying; quickness of motion
   In her <u>haste</u>, she was careless, so she tripped and spilled the water.

motionless [MOH shun lis] *adj.* still; not moving
   When the river freezes, the water on the surface becomes <u>motionless</u>.

overcome [oh vuhr KUM] *v.* defeated; conquered; overpowered by
   The weak line of defenders was quickly <u>overcome</u> by the opposing forces.

shatter [SHAT uhr] *v.* break into many pieces
   That fragile vase will <u>shatter</u> if it falls on the stone floor.

superb [soo PERB] *adj.* excellent; rich
   My grandfather's barbecue sauce is so <u>superb</u> that it often wins first prize.

Word List B

cinches [SIN chiz] *v.* tightens by pulling in
   A tight string <u>cinches</u> the bag of rice shut.

conscientious [kahn shee EN shuhs] *adj.* careful; doing what is right
   Reporting a lost wallet to the authorities is the <u>conscientious</u> thing to do.

eased [EEZD] *v.* comforted; lessened pain or other difficulty
   The powerful fan <u>eased</u> the heat in our attic.

infirm [in FERM] *adj.* weak; unwell
   <u>Infirm</u> patients recover in the hospital's rehabilitation area.

objector [ub JEK ter] *n.* one who opposes or is against something
   He is an <u>objector</u> to the new law because he does not think it is just.

route [ROOT] *n.* path; road
   We took a side <u>route</u> because the main road was blocked by snow.

Poetry Collection: Edna St. Vincent Millay, Dahlia Ravikovitch, and Emily Dickinson
Vocabulary Warm-up Exercises

Exercise A *Fill in each blank in the paragraph with an appropriate word from Word List A.*
Use each word only once.

I was out shopping for our family's groceries, but I was rushing to get home in

time for dinner. In my [1] _____, I forgot to buy the main ingredient:

chicken. When I discovered my mistake, I could not believe it. I stood in the

kitchen [2] _____, momentarily paralyzed. At first, I was totally

[3] _____ by the situation, but then decided I would make the best of it. I

modified the recipe [4] _____, one small change at a time. Before I knew

it, I had made a delicious chicken stew, minus the chicken. Carefully, I brought the

bowls to the table. I knew that they would [5] _____ if I dropped them,

and I had made enough mistakes for one day. The stew was a hit! My brother said it was

so [6] _____ I could serve it at a restaurant.

Exercise B *Write two sentences of your own for each word on Word List B. You may use a*
different form of the vocabulary word for your second sentence.

Example: *infirm*
    A. *During flu season, <u>infirm</u> students should rest and drink plenty of water.*
    B. *A nurse took care of the patients in the <u>infirmary</u>.*

1. route
    A. _____
    B. _____

2. objector
    A. _____
    B. _____

3. eased
    A. _____
    B. _____

4. conscientious
    A. _____
    B. _____

5. cinches
    A. _____
    B. _____

Name _____ Date _____

Poetry Collection: Edna St. Vincent Millay, Dahlia Ravikovitch, and Emily Dickinson
Reading Warm-up A

Read the following passage. Pay special attention to the underlined words. Then, read it again, and complete the activities. Use a separate sheet of paper for your written answers.

Imagine a huge boulder sitting proudly on a beach, holding the same position day and night, as <u>motionless</u> as a photograph. Hard and solid, it looks as if it will never change, but do not be deceived by appearances. Nature does not stand still, and there are many forces that will <u>overcome</u> this boulder's weighty pride. Erosion and weathering will cause many changes. Some will happen slowly, others can happen instantly.

Weathering breaks down rocks; erosion moves weathered rock from place to place. Weathering and erosion often affect rocks very <u>gradually</u>, so that the changes are not noticeable for many years. Waves carrying small bits of rock and shell beat against the boulder on the beach. These small pieces scrape against the boulder, sometimes removing even tinier pieces. The wind that whips against the rock's surface can also carry small particles that can erode the mighty boulder. Chemicals in the rain might eat away at the rock. Over time, the boulder slowly shrinks.

Nature is not always patient, however, and sometimes erosion makes changes in <u>haste</u>. Our boulder on the beach might look quite different in just a few moments. Ice wedging is a <u>superb</u> example of this type of sudden erosion. When the conditions are right for ice wedging, a few seconds are all it takes. Many boulders have tiny cracks that can trap water. If the temperature drops to freezing, this water will turn to ice. Water expands when it freezes, and this creates pressure against the rock. Over time, this process weakens the rock until one day water in the cracks will freeze again and suddenly the rock will <u>shatter</u>. It will break apart into two or more pieces. The newly formed chunks of rock appear to be permanent, but we know that this is only an appearance. The forces of nature are already working to break down the seemingly unbreakable.

1. Underline the words that mean the same thing as <u>motionless</u>. Then, describe something else that only seems to be *motionless*.

2. Underline the words that tell what nature's forces <u>overcome</u>. Then, tell what *overcome* means.

3. Underline the words that describe the changes that happen <u>gradually</u>. Then, tell something you can do *gradually*.

4. Circle the word that means the opposite of <u>haste</u>. Then, tell what *haste* means.

5. Underline the sentence that tells why ice wedging is a <u>superb</u> example of sudden erosion. Then, describe a place you have seen that you think is *superb*.

6. Underline the words that explain what happens when the boulder finally does <u>shatter</u>. Then, describe something else that might *shatter*.

Poetry Collection: Edna St. Vincent Millay, Dahlia Ravikovitch, and Emily Dickinson
Reading Warm-up B

Read the following passage. Pay special attention to the underlined words. Then, read it again, and complete the activities. Use a separate sheet of paper for your written answers.

In the first century A.D., a Roman doctor named Soranus used poetry to heal his patients. He found that comedy <u>eased</u> the minds of people who were depressed and tragedy calmed those with too much energy. Some modern therapists still use poetry therapy.

Poetry therapy aids healing or personal growth. People who are <u>infirm</u> or in poor health can benefit from poetry's rich language in many ways. They might read poetry that helps them deal with difficult emotions. They might write their own poetry to explore deep feelings. A <u>conscientious</u> poetry therapist carefully selects the best poems for each patient. One patient may flourish by reading poems about strong emotions like anger, fear, and jealousy, but another might be upset by these poems.

Therapists often need to overcome their patients' negative feelings about poetry. An <u>objector</u> might refuse to read poetry at all, thinking it dull or uninteresting. An effective therapist will find ways to persuade these patients, such as choosing timely poems. For example, *Giving Sorrow Words* is an online collection published by the National Association for Poetry Therapy. It presents poems that can help people respond to the attacks on the World Trade Center on September 11, 2001.

Poetry therapy often takes place in groups, where members sharing their writing. This <u>route</u> takes the participants on a path toward understanding themselves and provides them with a growing sense of community. As poet Myra Cohn Livingston has pointed out, poetry can "ease the aloneness which we all share in common." For writers in a poetry therapy group, the goal is not to create a poem that will dazzle readers. Instead, they hope to use their poems to share feelings and ideas that can be difficult to express.

Society confines our creativity the way a belt <u>cinches</u> in a wide waist. Writing poetry can be a wonderful release, like unbuckling a too-tight belt and finally breathing freely.

1. Circle the word that is a synonym for <u>eased</u>. Then, tell what *eased* means.

2. Underline the words that describe people who are <u>infirm</u>. Then, explain why you may not be able to tell if someone is *infirm* by looking at him or her.

3. Underline the words that tell what a <u>conscientious</u> therapist does. Then, explain a situation in which it is important to be *conscientious*.

4. Underline the words that tell what an <u>objector</u> might do. Then, tell what an *objector* is.

5. Circle the word that is a synonym for <u>route</u>. Then, describe the *route* you take to school.

6. Circle the words that tell what the belt <u>cinches</u>. Then, explain what *cinches* means.

Name _____ Date _____

Poetry Collection: Edna St. Vincent Millay, Dahlia Ravikovitch, and Emily Dickinson
Literary Analysis: Figurative Language

Figurative language is language that is not meant to be taken literally. Poets often use **figures of speech** to convey their ideas in fresh and innovative ways. Figurative language includes these devices:

- A **simile** is a comparison of unlike things using the words *like* or *as*.
- In a **metaphor,** one thing is spoken about as if it were something else.
- In **personification,** an object, animal, or idea is spoken of as if it were human.

Because figurative language is often used to express meaning in concrete pictures, it is an important source of **imagery,** or word-pictures, in poetry.

Read this line from "Pride."

  And suddenly the rock has an open wound.

Notice the use of metaphor, in which emotional pain is spoken of as "an open wound." The poet also personifies rocks.

A. DIRECTIONS: *Complete the following chart by recording examples of each type of figurative language from the poems in this grouping. If there are not two examples of a type of figurative language, include only one.*

Simile		
Metaphor		
Personification		

B. DIRECTIONS: *On the following lines, use each form of figurative language to describe an animal of your choice.*

Animal: _____

Simile: _____

Metaphor: _____

Personification: _____

Poetry Collection: Edna St. Vincent Millay, Dahlia Ravikovitch, and Emily Dickinson

Reading: Picture Imagery to Paraphrase Poems

To understand a poem, **paraphrase** it, or restate the meaning of lines in your own words. Begin by **picturing the imagery,** forming clear pictures of the descriptive details in the poem. Then, consider how the lines you will paraphrase are connected with these pictures.

Look at these lines from "Pride."

And so the moss flourishes, the seaweed / whips around, / the sea pushes through and rolls back—

You might picture waves crashing against a moss-covered rock. This can help you paraphrase the line as, "Rocks, like people, experience weathering over time."

DIRECTIONS: *Describe the image that each quotation in the following chart creates. Then, restate the line in your own words.*

Quotation	Image	Paraphrase
1. But I will not hold the bridle while he cinches the girth. (Millay)		
2. They don't move, so the cracks stay hidden. (Ravikovitch)		
3. The Truth must dazzle gradually (Dickinson)		

Poetry Collection: Edna St. Vincent Millay, Dahlia Ravikovitch, and Emily Dickinson

Vocabulary Builder

Word List

flourishes   circuit

A. DIRECTIONS: *On the following lines, write three examples that illustrate each word. For instance, if the word were* ingenious, *you might write* an imaginative inventor, a car that runs on vegetable oil, *or* a solution to an impossible math problem.

1. flourishes

   Example 1: _____

   Example 2: _____

   Example 3: _____

2. circuit

   Example 1: _____

   Example 2: _____

   Example 3: _____

B. DIRECTIONS: *Create two different sentences for each of the following words.*

1. flourishes

   _____

   _____

2. circuit

   _____

   _____

C. DIRECTIONS: *Find the pair of words that best expresses a relationship similar to that expressed in the pair in capital letters. Circle the letter of your choice.*

1. CIRCUIT: ORBIT
   A. moon: sun
   B. snow: wind
   C. circle: square
   D. cavern: cave
2. FLOURISHES: WILTS
   A. smiles: frowns
   B. skips: jumps
   C. grows: blooms
   D. harvests: reaps

Poetry Collection: Edna St. Vincent Millay, Dahlia Ravikovitch, and Emily Dickinson
Support for Writing a Critical Essay

Before you begin writing your critical essay, determine what criteria you will use to evaluate the poems. Fill in the following chart with criteria for evaluating the poems, your evaluation of the poems, and quotations that support your evaluation.

Criteria for Evaluation: _____

_____

	Evaluation	Quotations
"Conscientious Objector"		
"Pride"		
"Tell all the Truth but tell it slant—"		

Now, use your notes to write your critical essay explaining which of these poems you found most effective.

Poetry Collection: Edna St. Vincent Millay, Dahlia Ravikovitch, and Emily Dickinson

Support for Extend Your Learning

Listening and Speaking

Write notes for your group discussion in the following chart. Include your opinion about Dickinson's advice, reasons for your opinion, and quotations or examples that support your reasons.

My Opinion: _____

Reasons	Examples

Research and Technology

Use the following flowchart to note the important events in Edna St. Vincent Millay's career. Be sure to write the events in chronological order.

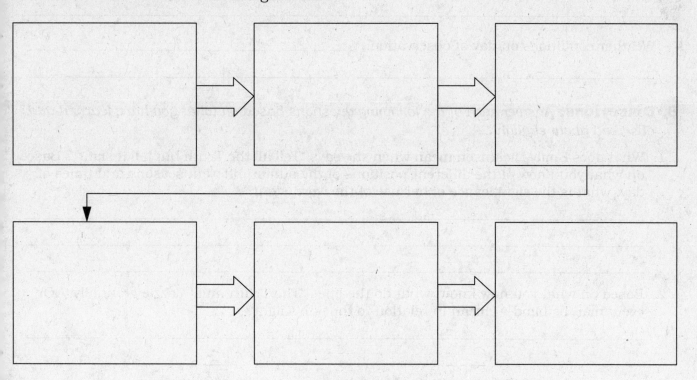

Name _____ Date _____

Poetry Collection: Edna St. Vincent Millay, Dahlia Ravikovitch, and Emily Dickinson
Enrichment: The Sun

"Tell all the Truth but tell it slant—" connects its theme to images of sunlight. The sun and its energy is a continual source of fascination for people on Earth. For about 4.6 billion years, this star at the center of our solar system has sustained life on Earth by providing it with light and heat. The sun's brilliant, fiery glow comes from nuclear reactions that take place at its center. What we call sunlight is light radiating from the sun that is visible at the Earth's surface. A variety of factors affect the way in which we experience the sun's radiation of light and heat. Remember that it is very dangerous to look directly into sunlight.

A. DIRECTIONS: *Make observations about the look and feel of the sun's light and warmth at different times of the day and under different weather conditions. Record your observations in the following chart.*

Early morning	
Midday	
Evening	

Weather conditions on day of observation: _____
_____

B. DIRECTIONS: *Answer each of the following questions based on what you have learned and observed about sunlight.*

1. What does Emily Dickinson mean when she says "Tell all the Truth but tell it slant"? Based on what you know of the different positions of the sun at different seasons and times of day, what is the significance of her use of the word *slant*?

   _____

   _____

   _____

2. Based on what you now know, what do the lines "The Truth must dazzle gradually / Or every man be blind—" mean in relation to the sun's light?

   _____

   _____

Poetry Collections: Yusef Komunyakaa, Eve Merriam, and Emily Dickinson;
Edna St. Vincent Millay, Dahlia Ravikovitch, and Emily Dickinson

Build Language Skills: Vocabulary Skill

Suffixes

The word *minimize* is built from the word root *-minim-* (small) and the verb-forming suffix *-ize*, meaning "to make, become, or engage in." Knowing the meanings of the word root and suffix helps you understand that *minimize* is a verb meaning "to make small." Other words containing the suffix *-ize* will also be verbs.

A. DIRECTIONS: *Change each of the following nouns to a verb by adding the -ize suffix. Then, use each verb in a sentence. Remember that the -ize suffix means "to make, become, or engage in." Note that when adding the suffix, some letters may have to be dropped or added: politics becomes* politicize, *for example. Check a dictionary if you need to.*

1. theory

   _____

2. character

   _____

3. drama

   _____

Academic Vocabulary Practice

distort	minimize	psychology	recur	drastic

B. DIRECTIONS: *Answer each question using the relevant academic vocabulary word.*

1. Why might someone want to study *psychology*?

   _____

2. If you have had chicken pox, is the illness likely to *recur*?

   _____

3. Why do political ads sometimes *distort* an opponent's ideas?

   _____

4. What is the most *drastic* weather event you have ever experienced?

   _____

5. Why is it important not to *minimize* the time you need to finish a project?

   _____

Poetry Collections: Yusef Komunyakaa, Eve Merriam, and Emily Dickinson;
Edna St. Vincent Millay, Dahlia Ravikovitch, and Emily Dickinson

Build Language Skills: Grammar

Prepositional Phrases

A **prepositional phrase** is a group of words that begins with a preposition and ends with a noun or pronoun.

A prepositional phrase that serves as an adjective is termed an *adjective phrase.* It modifies a noun or pronoun and tells *what kind* or *which one.*

> **Adjective Phrase:** The woman *in the blue dress* is a singer.

A prepositional phrase that serves as an adverb is termed an *adverb phrase.* It modifies a noun or pronoun and tells *what kind* or *which one.*

> **Adverb Phrase:** Her music group sings *at the folk festival.*

A. PRACTICE: *Underline the prepositional phrase in each of the following sentences. Then, write whether it is used as an* adjective *or* adverb.

_____ 1. The baseball players have their best moments on the ballfield.

_____ 2. The wind is compared to a tired man.

_____ 3. The conscientious objector refuses to give in to Death.

_____ 4. The rocks in the poem represent human feeling.

_____ 5. If you are too honest, the truth can be painful to the listener.

_____ 6. The metaphor in the third verse is striking.

_____ 7. The seal brushes against the rocks and cracks them.

_____ 8. Death flicks his whip at the speaker.

B. Writing Application: *Write four sentences about the poems in this collection. Use a prepositional phrase in each sentence. Underline the prepositional phrases.*

1. _____

2. _____

3. _____

4. _____

Poetry Collection: Edna St. Vincent Millay, Dahlia Ravikovitch, and Emily Dickinson
Selection Test A

Critical Reading *Identify the letter of the choice that best answers the question.*

____ 1. In "Conscientious Objector," who is the speaker's adversary?
   A. war
   B. slavery
   C. fear
   D. death

____ 2. What is the tone of "Conscientious Objector"?
   A. defiant
   B. happy
   C. comic
   D. despairing

____ 3. Which of these lines from "Conscientious Objector" contains an example of personification?
   A. "I shall die, but that is all that I shall do for Death."
   B. "He has business in Cuba, business in the / Balkans"
   C. "The password and the plans of our city are safe / with me"
   D. "Never through me / Shall you be overcome."

____ 4. What image do these lines from "Conscientious Objector" create?
   Though he flick my shoulders with his whip, I will not tell / him which way the fox ran.

   A. a funeral procession
   B. a dog chasing after a fox
   C. a carriage riding through a park
   D. a man whipping a horse to make it run faster

____ 5. Who is the "Brother" whom the speaker refers to in "Conscientious Objector"?
   A. death
   B. all humankind
   C. soldiers
   D. the speaker's actual brother

____ 6. In "Pride," what are the rocks a metaphor for?
   A. the sea
   B. humans
   C. the earth
   D. seals

_____ 7. In "Pride," what happens when the seal rubs against the rocks?
   A. The rocks age.
   B. The seal dies.
   C. The rocks break.
   D. The sea comes in.

_____ 8. What do the cracks in the rocks represent in "Pride"?
   A. human pride
   B. the passage of time
   C. broken bones
   D. people's troubles and hurts

_____ 9. In "Tell all the Truth but tell it slant—," what will happen if truth does not "dazzle gradually"?
   A. People will die.
   B. People will go blind.
   C. Rain will fall.
   D. Lightning will strike.

_____ 10. What image does this line from "Tell all the Truth but tell it slant—" create?
      The Truth must dazzle gradually
   A. a sudden storm
   B. a group of blind men
   C. a slow-growing bright light
   D. a dark room

_____ 11. In "Tell all the Truth but tell it slant—," to what is truth compared?
   A. light
   B. children
   C. rainfall
   D. mountains

Vocabulary and Grammar

_____ 12. Which of the following words has the same meaning as *flourishes*?
   A. sinks   C. thrives
   B. waves   D. wilts

_____ 13. Which of the following is a synonym for *distort*?
   A. twist   C. glow
   B. shine   D. crack

____ **14.** Which words in the following sentence are a prepositional phrase?

The truth can be painful if you do not temper it with kindness.

 A. if you do not   **C.** with kindness

 B. temper it   **D.** can be painful

____ **15.** Which words in the following sentence are a prepositional phrase?

The sun set completely, and we walked back from the pier.

 A. from the pier   **C.** we walked

 B. set completely   **D.** back from

Essay

16. In the poem "Tell all the Truth but tell it slant—," Dickinson uses a metaphor to create an image of truth. In an essay, describe the metaphor she uses. Why has she chosen this comparison? What does it say about Dickinson's feelings about truth? Support your claims with details from the poem.

17. Both "Conscientious Objector" and "Pride" use imagery to get a message across to the reader. In an essay, choose one of the poems and restate its message in your own words. Explain how the images in the poem help to create and strengthen the message.

Poetry Collection: Edna St. Vincent Millay, Dahlia Ravikovitch, and Emily Dickinson
Selection Test B

Critical Reading *Identify the letter of the choice that best completes the statement or answers the question.*

_____ 1. In "Conscientious Objector," the speaker's adversary is
   A. war.
   B. slavery.
   C. fear.
   D. death.

_____ 2. The tone of "Conscientious Objector" is
   A. defiant.
   B. respectful.
   C. wistful.
   D. despairing.

_____ 3. In "Conscientious Objector," why will the speaker not reveal the whereabouts of her enemies?
   A. She cannot reliably know where her enemies might be.
   B. Her enemies are human and, like her, have a greater enemy.
   C. She has taken a vow of silence and will not break it.
   D. She has not been promised enough to make the risk worthwhile.

_____ 4. Who is the "Brother" referred to at the end of "Conscientious Objector"?
   A. her adversary
   B. her actual brother
   C. the boy in the swamp
   D. her fellow man

_____ 5. What is the best way to paraphrase these lines from "Conscientious Objector"?
   Though he promise me much, I will not map him the route / to any man's door.

   A. Death has promised to bring me along on his route if I map it.
   B. Death may make me promises, but I will not help him.
   C. I have promised to bring Death to any man's door.
   D. Death has promised me a map showing the route to any man's door.

_____ 6. Which of these lines from "Conscientious Objector" is the best example of a metaphor?
   A. "Am I a spy in the land of the living . . ."
   B. "I shall die, but that is all that I shall do for Death."
   C. "I am not / on his pay-roll."
   D. "Shall you be overcome."

_____ 7. In the poem "Pride," what do the cracks in the rocks stand for?
   A. faults or weaknesses that everyone has
   B. unkind thoughts or wrongdoings of people
   C. troubles or hurts that people suppress because of pride
   D. pride itself, which can cause damage when someone has too much of it

____ 8. Why does the speaker in "Pride" say "it almost seems peaceful" when describing how the rocks lie on their backs for so many years?
A. Because the rocks lie there, the speaker describes them as if they were alive.
B. The rocks lie still, but the cracks have already begun to form.
C. The rocks would be peaceful except that they are lying in the heat and the cold.
D. The speaker is referring to how peaceful it is to see rocks lying on the seashore.

____ 9. Which of the following lines from "Pride" looks ahead to the seal's visit?
A. "For years they lie on their backs / in the heat and the cold,"
B. "Years pass over them, waiting."
C. "Whoever is going to shatter them / hasn't come yet."
D. "And so the moss flourishes,"

____ 10. What is the best way to paraphrase these lines from "Pride"?
And so the moss flourishes, the seaweed / whips around, / the sea pushes through and rolls back— / the rocks seem motionless.
A. The moss and the seaweed grow as the rocks are pushed back and forth.
B. Time passes and the rocks seem not to move, though moss grows on them and the sea moves back and forth.
C. The sea remains calm as the moss and seaweed die.
D. The sea whips the ship back and forth, while sailors toss moss and seaweed overboard.

____ 11. In "Pride," for what is the "little seal" a metaphor?
A. savage cruelty
B. the last straw
C. a great weight
D. the passage of time

____ 12. What is the best way to paraphrase these lines from "Tell all the Truth but tell it slant—"?
As Lightning to the Children eased / With explanation kind / The Truth must dazzle gradually
A. Just as an explanation makes lightning less scary to children, so truth should be explained gradually.
B. Lightning dazzles children, and the truth will dazzle them, too.
C. Truth is like an explanation of lightning to a child.
D. If the truth is told gradually, it can be as dangerous and scary to children as lightning is.

____ 13. In "Tell all the Truth but tell it slant—," what does Dickinson mean when she says that truth must be told at a "slant"?
A. People should lie.
B. Truth should be at an angle.
C. Truth should be told gently, not harshly.
D. People should be brutally honest.

____ 14. According to Dickinson, what will happen if truth does not "dazzle gradually"?
A. People will become dishonest.
B. People will become blinded.
C. Lightning will strike.
D. Truth will slant.

____ 15. In the central metaphor of "Tell all the Truth but tell it slant—," truth is compared to
   A. a rainstorm.
   B. jewels.
   C. children.
   D. sunlight.

Vocabulary and Grammar

____ 16. In the following line from "Tell all the Truth but tell it slant—," what does the word *circuit* mean?

   Success in Circuit lies

   A. a roundabout route   C. a straight line
   B. a good guess   D. a lightning strike

____ 17. In the following line from "Pride," what does the word *flourishes* mean?

   And so the moss flourishes, . . .

   A. drowns   C. thrives
   B. weakens   D. dies

____ 18. If you want to *minimize* the amount you eat, you must
   A. eat more.   C. eat different food.
   B. eat less.   D. eat at a different time.

____ 19. Which of the following sentences contains a prepositional phrase?
   A. Death rides his horse wildly.
   B. Death rides from village to city.
   C. Death cracks his whip.
   D. Death is the enemy the speaker hates.

____ 20. In which sentence is a prepositional phrase used as an adjective?
   A. The seal in the water moves softly.
   B. The seal brushes against the rock.
   C. The rock cracks after the seal touches it.
   D. The rock weathers in heat and cold.

Essay

21. In an essay, analyze the message of "Pride." First, state the message you believe Ravikovitch is communicating through the poem. Then, explain how she supports that message. How does she use metaphor to get her idea across? Does Ravikovitch succeed in convincing readers of the message?

22. In an essay, discuss Emily Dickinson's approach to expressing truth in "Tell all the Truth but tell it slant—." In your essay, address the following questions: What specific details convey the idea that speaking and knowing truth is important? What does the poet mean when she says, "Tell all the Truth but tell it slant—" and "The Truth must dazzle gradually. . . ."? How does Dickinson's central metaphor help support her ideas?

Vocabulary Warm-up Word Lists

Study these words from the poetry of Hughes, McCrae, and Sandburg. Then, apply your knowledge to the activities that follow.

Word List A

chords [KAWRDZ] *n.* groups of three or more tones sounded together
She played two <u>chords</u> on the piano—one beautiful, the other quite jarring.

croon [KROON] *v.* sing, especially in a soft or sentimental way
My uncle can <u>croon</u> a song so sweetly you will think you are dreaming.

mellow [MEL oh] *adj.* soft, rich, and full
The glowing fire and the quiet, romantic music created a <u>mellow</u> mood.

quarrel [KWAWR uhl] *n.* cause for disagreement
The brothers had a <u>quarrel</u> over whose turn it was to mow the lawn.

sob [SAHB] *v.* cry
My baby sister will <u>sob</u> if you take away her new toy.

weary [WEER ee] *adj.* tired; worn out
The traveler is <u>weary</u> after walking all day on a dirt road.

Word List B

amid [uh MID] *prep.* in the middle of
We could not hear the speech <u>amid</u> the cheering and laughing of the crowd.

droning [DROH ning] *v.* making a continuous humming noise
The loud <u>droning</u> of the fan motor was driving me crazy.

drowsy [DROW zee] *adj.* sleepy; half asleep
We put the <u>drowsy</u> children to bed before they fell asleep on the couch.

echoed [EK ohd] *v.* repeated again and again
The beautiful melody <u>echoed</u> in my head long after the concert ended.

foe [FOH] *n.* enemy
It is not necessarily true that someone who is not your friend must be a <u>foe</u>.

lonesome [LOHN suhm] *adj.* feeling unhappy at being alone
I felt <u>lonesome</u> in the strange city, so I called my best friend to chat.

Poetry Collection: Langston Hughes, John McCrae, Carl Sandburg
Vocabulary Warm-up Exercises

Exercise A *Fill in each blank in the paragraph with an appropriate word from Word List A.*
Use each word only once.

Tanya and Riley were best friends, but they were in the middle of a big argument. The

[1] _____ began because they could not agree on a radio station. They

switched back and forth between two stations so many times that they were both

[2] _____ of the battle. Tanya was so frustrated she started to

[3] _____, but she wiped away her tears and decided to try another

approach. "Maybe we should try a brand new station," she suggested. She moved the

dial to a station that neither friend had ever heard before. A deep voice was just starting

to [4] _____ a slow ballad. The [5] _____ of the music were

simple, but the effect was beautiful. In just a few minutes, the new station had changed

the mood in the room from angry to [6] _____.

Exercise B *Decide whether each statement is true or false. Explain your answers.*

1. Joining a club might help someone feel less <u>lonesome</u>.
   T / F _____

2. Every <u>foe</u> is equally dangerous.
   T / F _____

3. It is common to feel <u>drowsy</u> after riding in a car for many hours.
   T / F _____

4. If you are <u>amid</u> a field in bloom, you cannot see any flowers.
   T / F _____

5. When a sound is <u>droning</u>, it is always extremely loud.
   T / F _____

6. If a shout <u>echoed</u> loudly, no one could have heard it.
   T / F _____

Poetry Collection: Langston Hughes, John McCrae, Carl Sandburg
Reading Warm-up A

Read the following passage. Pay special attention to the underlined words. Then, read it again, and complete the activities. Use a separate sheet of paper for your written answers.

Blues music is a kind of jazz that began in the southern United States, rooted in African American work chants and religious songs called *spirituals*. The themes of blues are sadness, worry, and despair. Blues singers are <u>weary</u> of the troubles they have seen. However, their music soars above those worries. As blues singer Mahalia Jackson explained, "Anybody that sings the blues is in a deep pit, yelling for help."

The blues follows a standard form. Musicians use this form in endless ways. The <u>chords</u>, or groups of notes played together, follow a predictable pattern, but the results are seldom boring. The form gives listeners and musicians a common starting place for an ever-changing musical journey.

Blues songs often tell about the singer's unhappy life. Blues singers use a variety of strategies to share these sad tales with listeners. One singer might <u>croon</u> in an elegant, beautiful voice while singing of a broken heart. For this singer, one deep, slow breath might reflect a lifetime of suffering. Another singer might bring the sorrow into the song more directly by using a rough and broken voice. This singer might break down in the middle of a song and <u>sob</u> an entire line, burying the words under heartfelt tears.

The blues allowed African Americans to express deep feelings that they often had to hide to survive. When blues was developing in the 1920s, it was rare for African Americans to have a direct <u>quarrel</u> with people in power. If they fought their harsh treatment, they would face worse consequences. The blues gave them a way to vent their anger and sadness. Singer Alberta Hunter commented, "Blues means what milk does to a baby. Blues is what the spirit is to the minister. We sing the blues because our hearts have been hurt, our souls have been disturbed." Even when blues music sounds <u>mellow</u>, the soft and comforting tune expresses deep pain.

1. Underline the words that tell what blues singers are <u>weary</u> of. Then, tell what *weary* means.

2. Circle the words that tell what <u>chords</u> are. Then, describe an instrument with which a person can play *chords*.

3. Underline the words that tell how one blues singer might <u>croon</u>. Then, explain what *croon* means.

4. Underline the words that tell what happens when a singer chooses to <u>sob</u> while singing. Then, describe a situation in which you might *sob*.

5. Underline the sentence that tells the reason for a possible <u>quarrel</u> and its possible result. Then, tell what a *quarrel* is.

6. Circle two words that are synonyms for <u>mellow</u>. Then, describe how to create a *mellow* mood at a party.

Poetry Collection: Langston Hughes, John McCrae, Carl Sandburg
Reading Warm-up B

Read the following passage. Pay special attention to the underlined words. Then, read it again, and complete the activities. Use a separate sheet of paper for your written answers.

When John McCrae wrote "In Flanders Fields" in 1915, no one knew that it would become one of the most famous war memorials of all time. He wrote the poem <u>amid</u> the chaos and tragedy of World War I.

When Britain went to war against Germany in 1914, Canada was part of the British Empire. Soon after the declaration of war, more than 45,000 Canadians joined the fight against Britain's enemy because it was also Canada's <u>foe</u>. Surgeon John McCrae was one of these new soldiers. Before leaving for the war front, he wrote, "I am really rather afraid, but more afraid to stay at home with my conscience."

Unfortunately, McCrae's experiences exceeded his worst fears. The fighting was constant and deadly. In a letter to his mother, McCrae described the tension of living under continuous attack, explaining how "gunfire and rifle fire never ceased for sixty seconds." The steady noise must have become a terrible <u>droning</u> as McCrae worked to heal the wounded soldiers. Then, one of McCrae's closest friends was killed. McCrae could only bury him in a makeshift grave under a simple wooden cross. The next day, McCrae wrote "In Flanders Fields" in memory of his friend and all those who had died.

In the poem's famous opening image, poppies blow between the soldiers' grave markers. These <u>lonesome</u> flowers without companions have become a symbol of the losses of wartime, yet many readers ask: Why poppies? Nature offers a simple answer: Wild poppies will bloom when other nearby plants are dead. The struggles of war had destroyed many plants. Soon, blood-red, wild poppies were the only plants growing. Poppies are also a symbol of sleep. McCrae uses poppies to compare <u>drowsy</u> people at rest with the bodies of the dead, which are forever still. In his poem, McCrae gives the dead a voice. Their memorable lines have <u>echoed</u> in the minds of readers for decades.

1. Underline the words that tell what McCrae was <u>amid</u> when he wrote his poem. Then, tell what *amid* means.

2. Circle a word that is a synonym for <u>foe</u>. Then, explain how you know if someone is your *foe*.

3. Circle the words that tell what made the <u>droning</u> sound. Then, describe a loud *droning* you have heard.

4. Underline the words that tell why the flowers are <u>lonesome</u>. Then, tell about a place where you might feel *lonesome*.

5. Circle the words that describe the <u>drowsy</u> people. Then, write about something that makes you feel *drowsy*.

6. Underline the words that tell whose lines <u>echoed</u>; circle the words that tell where they *echoed*. Then, write a sentence about something you remember that *echoed*.

Name _____ Date _____

Poetry Collection: Langston Hughes, John McCrae, and Carl Sandburg
Literary Analysis: Sound Devices

To spark the music in words, poets use a variety of **sound devices,** or patterns of word-sounds. These include alliteration, assonance, consonance, and onomatopoeia. **Alliteration** is the repetition of consonant sounds at the beginnings of nearby words, as in "silent song." **Assonance** is the repetition of vowel sounds in nearby stressed syllables, as in "deep and dreamless." Unlike rhyming syllables, assonant syllables end in different consonants. **Consonance** is the repetition of consonant sounds at the ends of nearby stressed syllables with different vowel sounds, as in "heat of lightning." **Onomatopoeia** is the use of words to imitate actual sounds, such as *buzz, tap,* or *splash.* Sound devices can add to the mood of a poem, imitate the sound of events, or reflect or emphasize a poem's meaning.

Read this line from "Jazz Fantasia."

Drum on your drums, batter on your banjoes, / sob on the long cool winding saxophones.

The *b* in *batter* and *banjoes* is an example of alliteration, the word *drum* is an example of onomatopoeia, and the *ng* sound in *long* and *winding* is an example of consonance. These sound devices help to create a musical sound in the poem.

DIRECTIONS: *Fill in the following chart with at least two examples of each sound device from the poems in this collection.*

Alliteration	Assonance	Consonance	Onomatopoeia

Poetry Collection: Langston Hughes, John McCrae, and Carl Sandburg
Reading: Break Down Long Sentences to Paraphrase Poems

To help you understand poetry, **paraphrase** poems, restating the ideas in your own words. First, **break down long sentences** into parts.

- Identify the main actions and who or what performs them.
- Identify details that show when, where, how, or why each action is performed.

Read the following sentence from "Jazz Fantasia."

  Sling your knuckles on the bottoms of the happy / tin pans, let your trombones ooze, and go husha- / husha-hush with the slippery sand-paper.

Who? musicians
Action: play music
Paraphrase: Musicians are playing jazz with tin pans, trombones, and sandpaper.

DIRECTIONS: *Paraphrase the following excerpts from the poems in this collection. Begin by identifying the main actions and who performs them.*

1. Down on Lenox Avenue the other night / By the pale dull pallor of an old gas light / He did a lazy sway. . . . / He did a lazy sway. . . . / To the tune o' those Weary Blues.

   (Hughes)

   Who? _____

   Action: _____

   Paraphrase: _____

   _____

2. Short days ago / We lived, felt dawn, saw sunset glow, / Loved and were loved, and now we lie / In Flanders Fields.

   (McCrae)

   Who? _____

   Action: _____

   Paraphrase: _____

   _____

3. Can the rough stuff . . . now a Mississippi steamboat / pushes up the night river with a hoo-hoo-hoo-oo . . . and / the green lanterns calling to the high soft stars . . . a red / moon rides on the humps of the low river hills . . . go to it, / O jazzmen.

   (Sandburg)

   Who? _____

   Action: _____

   Paraphrase: _____

   _____

Unit 4 Resources: Poetry

Name _____ Date _____

Poetry Collection: Langston Hughes, John McCrae, and Carl Sandburg
Vocabulary Builder

Word List

```
pallor      ebony      melancholy
```

A. DIRECTIONS: *Read the following sentences and fill in each blank with the most appropriate word from the list.*

1. The _____ keys on the piano are the sharps and flats.
2. The saxophone created a(n) _____ sound that caused several people in the audience to cry.
3. The musician's _____ showed that he had not been outdoors for weeks.

B. DIRECTIONS: *Follow the directions to write a sentence using each word.*

1. Use *ebony* in a sentence about a jazz club.

_____

_____

2. Use *melancholy* in a sentence about a song you have heard.

_____

_____

3. Use *pallor* in a sentence about a person who is not feeling well.

_____

_____

C. DIRECTIONS: *Find the word that is most similar in meaning to the word in CAPITAL LETTERS. Circle the letter of your choice.*

1. EBONY
   A. hard   C. pale
   B. black   D. sharp
2. PALLOR
   A. paleness   C. death
   B. weakness   D. darkness
3. MELANCHOLY
   A. absent   C. gloomy
   B. musical   D. confused

Poetry Collection: Langston Hughes, John McCrae, and Carl Sandburg
Support for Writing a Poem

Before you begin to write your poem, fill in the following idea web with details you can include in your poem.

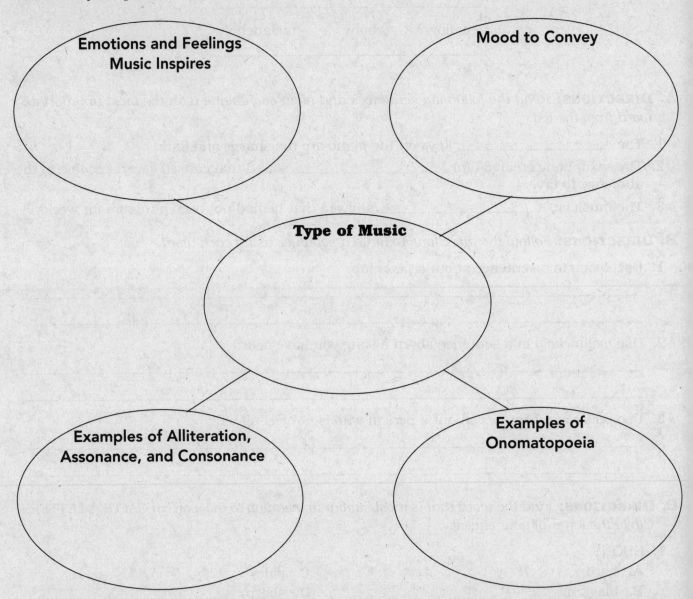

Now, use the details you have collected to write your poem about your favorite kind of music.

Name _____   Date _____

Poetry Collection: Langston Hughes, John McCrae, and Carl Sandburg
Support for Extend Your Learning

Listening and Speaking

On the following lines, write down the poets and poems you listened to. Then, write your reactions to the readings.

Poet 1: _____

Poems: _____

My reaction: _____

_____

Poet 2: _____

Poems: _____

My reaction: _____

_____

Poet 3: _____

Poems: _____

My reaction: _____

_____

Research and Technology

On the following lines, write the name of the artist and the artworks you have chosen to compare with Langston Hughes's poem. Then, list similarities and differences between the poem and the artworks.

Artist: _____

Works: _____

Similarities: _____

_____

Differences: _____

_____

Poetry Collection: Langston Hughes, John McCrae, and Carl Sandburg
Enrichment: Jazz and Blues

Two of the poems in this collection concern themselves with forms of music native to America. Both jazz and blues as distinct forms originated in the African American world of the nineteenth century, but have roots much older, from Africa and Europe. The combining of West African rhythms and cadences with European forms such as hymns and marches led to a new type of music in America.

Jazz has as its hallmark a dependence on improvisation. The music is fluid and rhythmically complex, including syncopation and conflicting rhythms from different instruments. Often jazz players pass the lead around, the soloist on each instrument improvising within the general chord progression.

One form of jazz has its roots in the blues, a style more closely linked to popular and folk music. Repeated lyrics dealing with hard lives and lost loves provide a framework for musical interpretation progressing through call and response patterns. These patterns were based on group vocal dynamics of work and religious origin. Blues and jazz overlap, but each has also developed independently.

DIRECTIONS: *Using your school or local library, read more about jazz and blues. Then, using library or online sources, listen to music by the following artists performing jazz or blues. Identify a piece and note its characteristics.*

Jazz Performer	Piece Performed	Characteristics
Jelly Roll Morton		
Louis Armstrong		
Duke Ellington		

Blues Performer	Piece Performed	Characteristics
B. B. King		
Bessie Smith		
Ray Charles		

Poetry Collection: Langston Hughes, John McCrae, and Carl Sandburg
Selection Test A

Critical Reading *Identify the letter of the choice that best answers the question.*

____ 1. What is the pianist in "The Weary Blues" doing when he makes the piano "moan with melody"?
   A. playing poorly though enthusiastically
   B. humming with the music
   C. playing sadly with feeling
   D. banging violently on the keys

____ 2. What are the blues that the pianist sings about in "The Weary Blues"?
   A. poverty
   B. labor
   C. hunger
   D. loneliness

____ 3. What is the speaker doing in "The Weary Blues"?
   A. playing a blues song
   B. singing a blues song
   C. listening to a blues song
   D. writing a blues song

____ 4. Which of these phrases from "The Weary Blues" shows an example of alliteration?
   A. "Down on Lenox Avenue"
   B. "Swaying to and fro"
   C. "that poor piano"
   D. "a deep song voice"

____ 5. Who is performing the action in these lines from "The Weary Blues"?

   Down on Lenox Avenue the other night / By the pale dull pallor of an old gas light / He did a lazy sway. . . . / He did a lazy sway. . . . / To the tune o' those Weary Blues.

   A. a musician
   B. the speaker
   C. someone in a dream
   D. someone on the street

____ 6. Which of these phrases from "In Flanders Fields" contains an example of assonance?

    A. "The torch; be yours to hold it high."

    B. "We shall not sleep"

    C. "We are the Dead"

    D. "In Flanders fields the poppies blow"

____ 7. Who are the speakers of "In Flanders Fields"?

    A. poppies in a cemetery

    B. soldiers killed in battle

    C. soldiers in battle

    D. relatives of soldiers

____ 8. What are the speakers asking of the reader in these lines from "In Flanders Fields"?

       To you from failing hands we throw / The torch; be yours to hold it high.

    A. to have faith in the speakers

    B. to plant poppies in Flanders Fields

    C. to carry on the speakers' fight

    D. to pray for those who died

____ 9. Who is performing the action in these lines from "Jazz Fantasia"?

       Moan like an autumn wind high in the lonesome treetops, / moan soft like you wanted somebody terrible. . . .

    A. the speaker of the poem

    B. a person who is crying

    C. a person in a dream

    D. a group of musicians

____ 10. What is the speaker in "Jazz Fantasia" doing?

    A. listening to a jazz band

    B. playing in a jazz band

    C. singing with a jazz band

    D. dancing to a jazz band

____ 11. Which of these phrases from "Jazz Fantasia" contains an example of onomatopoeia?

    A. "make two people fight"

    B. "batter on your banjoes"

    C. "the green lanterns calling"

    D. "a racing car slipping away"

_____ **12.** When the speaker tells the musicians in "Jazz Fantasia" to "Can the rough stuff," what does he want them to do?
  A. play on cans
  B. play more softly
  C. stop playing
  D. play more roughly

Vocabulary and Grammar

_____ **13.** What does the word *melancholy* mean in the following line from "The Weary Blues"?

  In a deep song voice with a melancholy tone

  A. sad   C. ill
  B. angry   D. perplexed

_____ **14.** What is *ideology* the study of?
  A. insects   C. music
  B. ideas   D. poetry

_____ **15.** In which sentence is an infinitive italicized?
  A. The singer went *to bed* when he finished singing.
  B. The poet tries *to create* a sense of the rhythm of jazz.
  C. The speakers talk *to the readers* about their deaths in Flanders.
  D. The speaker listens *to a man* singing a weary song.

Essay

16. In an essay, paraphrase the poem "In Flanders Fields." Restate the poem in your own words. Refer to details from the poem that tell you the main action and who performs it. Identify details that show where and why each action is performed.

17. "The Weary Blues" and "Jazz Fantasia" use sound devices to create a sense of the music they describe. In an essay, explain what sound devices each poet uses and describe how the use of the sound devices contributes to the mood of the musical form in each poem. Use details from the poems to support your conclusions.

Poetry Collection: Langston Hughes, John McCrae, and Carl Sandburg
Selection Test B

Critical Reading *Identify the letter of the choice that best completes the statement or answers the question.*

____ 1. The setting of "The Weary Blues" is
   A. a blues festival in New Orleans.
   B. a nightclub on Lenox Avenue.
   C. a steamboat on the Mississippi.
   D. a dark street lit by a gas lamp.

____ 2. How could you paraphrase these lines from "The Weary Blues"?
   By the pale dull pallor of an old gas light / He did a lazy sway. . . . / He did a lazy sway. . . . / To the tune o' those Weary Blues.

   A. A musician played the Weary Blues with feeling.
   B. A musician sang the Weary Blues during the middle of the day.
   C. One night, I dreamed I heard a musician play the Weary Blues.
   D. I sang the Weary Blues last night.

____ 3. What sound devices does Hughes use in this line from "The Weary Blues"?
   He made that poor piano moan with melody.

   A. assonance and alliteration
   B. consonance and onomatopoeia
   C. alliteration and onomatopoeia
   D. assonance and consonance

____ 4. How could you paraphrase these lines from "In Flanders Fields"?
   Short days ago / We lived, felt dawn, saw sunset glow / Loved and were loved, and now we lie / In Flanders fields.

   A. Yesterday we could see, but now we have become blind in battle.
   B. Not long ago we were alive, but now we are dead and buried in Flanders fields.
   C. We lived only a short time and saw few dawns and sunsets.
   D. A few days ago we were in love, but now we lie in Flanders fields.

____ 5. From where are the speakers of "In Flanders Fields" speaking?
   A. camps in Flanders
   B. graves in Flanders
   C. battlefields all over Europe
   D. their postwar homes

____ 6. What sound devices does McCrae use in the following line from "In Flanders Fields"?
   To you from failing hands we throw / The torch. . . .

   A. onomatopoeia and assonance
   B. consonance and alliteration
   C. assonance and alliteration
   D. onomatopoeia and consonance

____ 7. In "In Flanders Fields," what does the poem's repetitive beat suggest?
A. soldiers carrying the torch of the fallen soldiers
B. the bravely singing larks and other birds that fly over Flanders fields
C. the sound of gunfire in Flanders fields
D. the rows and rows of grave markers throughout Flanders fields

____ 8. "Jazz Fantasia" creates its impression by
A. conveying a humorous and ironic tone.
B. describing the troubles of the musicians.
C. using sound devices to capture the music.
D. listing various nontraditional instruments.

____ 9. Images of love, a car chase, and a fight in "Jazz Fantasia" suggest
A. the genuine feelings that jazz expresses.
B. the negative reputation of the music.
C. the hectic personal lives of most musicians.
D. the subjects discussed in jazz songs.

____ 10. The tone of the section in "Jazz Fantasia" relating to the steamboat is
A. ironic.
B. gentle.
C. historic.
D. angry.

____ 11. How could you best paraphrase the following lines from "Jazz Fantasia"?
Sling your knuckles on the bottoms of the happy / tin pans, let your trombones ooze, and go husha- / husha-hush with the slippery sand-paper.

A. Sling your knuckles, ooze your trombones, go husha-husha-hush.
B. Hit the tin pans on their bottoms with your knuckles.
C. Play music on the tin pans, the trombones, and the sandpaper.
D. Use the sandpaper to make a sound like husha-husha-hush.

____ 12. At the end of "Jazz Fantasia," what does the speaker tell the musicians to do?
A. play softer
B. play louder
C. stop playing
D. listen instead of playing

____ 13. Which of these phrases from "Jazz Fantasia" contains an example of alliteration?
A. "Sling your knuckles"
B. "batter on your banjoes"
C. "Can the rough stuff"
D. "the green lanterns calling"

Vocabulary and Grammar

____ 14. The word *pallor* means
A. flabbiness.   C. meeting.
B. paleness.   D. boredom.

____ 15. Songs in the tradition of the blues are often *melancholy.* In other words, they are
A. passionate.   C. religious.
B. joyful.   D. gloomy.

____ 16. Which of the following is the best meaning of the word *recur* as it is used in the following sentence?

A storm as violent as last week's is unlikely to *recur* in the near future.

A. terminate   C. be as extreme
B. lessen   D. happen again

____ 17. In the following sentence, the infinitive phrase "to help her" functions as an
_____ to modify the word _____.

Anita asked Lanie to help her.

A. adjective; Lanie   C. adverb; Anita
B. adverb; asked   D. adjective; Anita

____ 18. In which sentence is the infinitive used as a noun?
A. To choose a game took over an hour.
B. Malika brought her book to class.
C. Marnie went to study at the library.
D. Cindy wanted someone to advise her.

____ 19. In which sentence is the infinitive used as an adjective?
A. Nobody knew where to go.
B. He expressed a need to sleep.
C. To finish the project took a full week.
D. Ellie wanted to go for a walk.

Essay

20. Carl Sandburg uses sound devices in "Jazz Fantasia" to reflect an appreciation for the art of jazz. In an essay, explain what sound devices Sandburg uses and describe how the use of the sound devices contributes to the jazz mood. Use details from the poem to back up your points.

21. In an essay, explain how "In Flanders Fields" focuses on the handing down of an important duty. Explain what has been handed down and what it means to the speakers of the poem.

Vocabulary Warm-up Word Lists

Study these words from the poetry of Tennyson, Browning, and Toomer. Then, apply your knowledge to the activities that follow.

Word List A

pane [PAYN] *n.* window; glass in a window or door
A softball smashed through the window, breaking the <u>pane</u> into many pieces.

reapers [REE puhrz] *n.* people who cut and gather crops
The <u>reapers</u> gathered the wheat into sheaves and stacked it in the field.

ringlets [RING litz] *n.* curls, especially of hair
The child's hair fell in long curly <u>ringlets</u>.

squealing [SKWEE ling] *v.* making a short high cry or shriek
As the <u>squealing</u> continued, we realized a raccoon was in the pigpen.

startled [STAHRT uhld] *v.* surprised
She was <u>startled</u> when the children ran laughing into the meditation room.

wondrous [WUN druhs] *adj.* amazing; wonderful
A perfect rose that has just bloomed is a <u>wondrous</u>, though short-lived, sight.

Word List B

abysmal [uh BIZ muhl] *adj.* bottomless; too deep for measurement
The wrecked boat had sunk down to the <u>abysmal</u> depths of the ocean.

continue [kuhn TIN yoo] *v.* keep going
Please <u>continue</u> painting the wall until the job is finished.

cove [KOHV] *n.* a small bay
We launched our raft from the sandy <u>cove</u> and sailed it out to the open sea.

lain [LAYN] *v.* was located at; rested at
The broken boat has <u>lain</u> at the bottom of the ocean for many years.

quench [KWENCH] *v.* put out; satisfy; get rid of
A bucket of water will <u>quench</u> most campfires.

slumbering [SLUM buhr ing] *adj.* sleeping
The <u>slumbering</u> cat reached out for a mouse that darted through its dream.

Poetry Collection: Alfred, Lord Tennyson; Robert Browning; Jean Toomer
Vocabulary Warm-up Exercises

Exercise A *Fill in each blank in the paragraph with an appropriate word from Word List A.*
Use each word only once.

Mona left the pen gate open by mistake. Before long, she heard the smallest pig

[1] _____ a high-pitched squeak as it ran out of the pen. She chased the

pig into the field, where the [2] _____ were clearing the last of the

cornstalks from the field. One of the workers was so [3] _____ when the

pig brushed his leg that he jumped into the air. Mona followed the trail of the runaway

pig into the barn. There, the pig ran into a rake, which fell over and crashed into a

[4] _____ of glass. The sound of breaking glass scared the pig, so it

ran into a pen where Mona's father was carefully shearing off a big sheep's curly

[5] _____. The little pig jumped on top of the sheep and stared at Mona.

She had to laugh when she saw this [6] _____ sight.

Exercise B *Write a sentence to answer each question. For each item, use a word from Word*
List B to replace each underlined word without changing its meaning.

Example: Is the water probably deeper in a <u>bay</u> or in the ocean?
Water is probably deeper in the ocean than in a <u>cove</u>.

1. When might you need to disturb someone who is <u>sleeping</u>?

   _____

2. Do you think could you retrieve a quarter that fell down a <u>deep</u> well?

   _____

3. How might researchers discover a shipwreck that has <u>rested</u> at the bottom of the
   sea for one hundred years?

   _____

4. If someone wants to become a better ice skater, how might he or she <u>keep</u>
   improving?

   _____

5. What is your favorite way to <u>satisfy</u> a strong thirst?

   _____

Poetry Collection: Alfred, Lord Tennyson; Robert Browning; Jean Toomer
Reading Warm-up A

Read the following passage. Pay special attention to the underlined words. Then, read it again, and complete the activities. Use a separate sheet of paper for your written answers.

Moonlight fell like a soft blanket over the empty field. I held the hem of my dress above the freshly chopped stalks. That afternoon, <u>reapers</u> had cut down and collected the tall wheat. I paced back and forth, trying not to think about the one question my mind could not stop asking: "Will he come to meet me?"

Minutes passed like hours until at last it was midnight, the time we had set. I closed my eyes and counted to one hundred, hoping for a <u>wondrous</u> sight, a marvelous gift. Instead, the same empty field appeared before my eyes. I shut them again, afraid for the first time that he might not keep his promise.

Then, it started to rain, as if nature decided to mock my tears. The shower was heavy enough to soak my hair, flattening all of the <u>ringlets</u> I had so carefully curled. Cold and wet, I stopped pacing, as if I had become a statue, a frozen portrait of waiting.

Suddenly, I was <u>startled</u> by a noise, a little tap that snapped me to life. There it was again—a small tapping in the distance! Could it be the step of his boots along a stony path? My heart began to pound excitedly. I heard another tap, and began to doubt. Yes, it could be a footstep, but it could just as easily be the scraping of a branch against a <u>pane</u> of glass in the barn.

Then, the noise stopped and time froze. In just a few moments, I would be <u>squealing</u> with joy, shrieking with excitement upon seeing him at the edge of the field, running toward me. Nonetheless, at that moment, time felt forever frozen. Often, before I fall asleep, I revisit that frozen moment in that empty field just before his arrival.

1. Underline the words that explain what the <u>reapers</u> had done. Then, explain what *reapers* are.

2. Circle the word that is a synonym for <u>wondrous</u>. Then, describe a *wondrous* sight that you have seen this year.

3. Underline the words that explain how the narrator created her <u>ringlets</u>. Then, describe what someone with hair in *ringlets* looks like.

4. Underline the words that tell what <u>startled</u> the narrator. Then, describe a time when someone you know was *startled*.

5. Circle the word that tells what the <u>pane</u> was made of. Then, explain what a *pane* is.

6. Circle the word that is a synonym for <u>squealing</u>. Then, tell what *squealing* means.

Poetry Collection: Alfred, Lord Tennyson; Robert Browning; Jean Toomer
Reading Warm-up B

Read the following passage. Pay special attention to the underlined words. Then, read it again, and complete the activities. Use a separate sheet of paper for your written answers.

In 1755, Erik Pontopiddan described a terrifying monster called a *kraken* in his *Natural History of Norway.* According to this writer, the underwater creature had lain for centuries at the bottom of the sea off the coast of Norway and Iceland. He described the Kraken as "the largest and most surprising of all the animal creation." He paints an amazing picture of a terrible beast more than a mile-and-a-half long that could easily pull the largest ship to the ocean bottom with its tentacles.

When he was 21, Alfred, Lord Tennyson wrote a poem about this legendary beast. He imagines the slumbering monster sleeping in the depths of the ocean, waiting to attack. While both descriptions of the kraken seem exaggerated, many scientists believe they were inspired by a real animal: the mysterious giant squid.

Much about the giant squid still remains unknown. These animals live in the abysmal depths of the ocean, where it is almost impossible to study them. What little we know is based on finding dead specimens. In 1878, three fishermen in Newfoundland, Canada, were amazed to discover that they had snagged a giant squid. Using their anchor as a hook, they dragged the beast to a cove and tied it to a tree. When the tide went out, the squid was stranded and died. That specimen measured about 35 feet long—a little longer than most school buses.

Many scientists want to learn more about this secret animal, hoping to quench their curiosity with real sightings and documentary evidence. Today, scientists have learned a handful of fascinating facts about these oddities. Giant squids can change color. They have eyes the size of dinnerplates, the largest eyes of any animal. They use lightweight ammonia instead of air to float in water. These interesting tidbits only add to researchers' curiosity, and the hunt for the giant squid will certainly continue until someone finally captures a living specimen of this elusive creature.

1. Underline the words that tell where the kraken had lain for centuries. Then, tell what *lain* means.

2. Circle the word that is a synonym for slumbering. Then, describe how you should treat a *slumbering* animal.

3. Underline the words that describe the abysmal depths. Then, explain what *abysmal* means.

4. Underline the words that explain why the squid died in the cove. Then, describe what a *cove* might look like.

5. Circle the words that tell what scientists hope to quench. Then, explain whether or not you think that they will ever achieve this goal.

6. Underline the words that tell what will continue. Then, describe something you plan to *continue* doing for the rest of this school year.

Poetry Collection: Alfred, Lord Tennyson; Robert Browning; and Jean Toomer
Literary Analysis: Sound Devices

To spark the music in words, poets use a variety of **sound devices,** or patterns of word-sounds. These include alliteration, assonance, consonance, and onomatopoeia. **Alliteration** is the repetition of consonant sounds at the beginnings of nearby words, as in "silent song." **Assonance** is the repetition of vowel sounds in nearby stressed syllables, as in "d*ee*p and dr*ea*mless." Unlike rhyming syllables, assonant syllables end in different consonants. **Consonance** is the repetition of consonant sounds at the ends of nearby stressed syllables with different vowel sounds, as in "hea*t* of ligh*t*ning." **Onomatopoeia** is the use of words to imitate actual sounds, such as *buzz, tap,* or *splash.* Sound devices can add to the mood of a poem, imitate the sound of events, or reflect or emphasize a poem's meaning.

Read this line from "Reapers."

And there, a field rat, startled, squealing bleeds

The *s* in *startled* and *squealing* is an example of alliteration; the word *squealing* is an example of onomatopoeia; the long *e* sound in *field, squealing,* and *bleeds* is an example of assonance. These sound devices help to create a grim, rhythmic feel that mimics the movement of the mower.

DIRECTIONS: *Fill in the following chart with at least two examples of each sound device from the poems in this collection.*

Alliteration	Assonance	Consonance	Onomatopoeia

Poetry Collection: Alfred, Lord Tennyson; Robert Browning; and Jean Toomer

Reading: Break Down Long Sentences to Paraphrase Poems

To help you understand poetry, **paraphrase** poems, restating the ideas in your own words. First, **break down long sentences** into parts.

- Identify the main actions and who or what performs them.
- Identify details that show when, where, how, or why each action is performed.

Read this sentence from "Reapers."

I see them place the hones / In their hip-pockets as a thing that's done, / And start their silent swinging, one by one.

Who? the reapers

Action: prepare to reap the field

Paraphrase: The reapers put their sharpeners in their pockets and begin to reap the field.

DIRECTIONS: *Paraphrase these excerpts by using the information above.*

1. There hath he lain for ages and will lie / Battening upon huge seaworms in his sleep, / Until the latter fire shall heat the deep; / Then once by man and angels to be seen, / In roaring he shall rise and on the surface die.

    (Tennyson)

    Who? _____

    Action: _____

    Paraphrase: _____

    _____

2. Then a mile of warm sea-scented beach; / Three fields to cross till a farm appears; / A tap at the pane, the quick sharp scratch / And blue spurt of a lighted match, / And a voice less loud, through its joys and fears, / Than the two hearts beating each to each!

    (Browning)

    Who? _____

    Action: _____

    Paraphrase: _____

    _____

3. Black horses drive a mower through the weeds, / And there, a field rat, startled, squealing bleeds. . . .

    (Toomer)

    Who? _____

    Action: _____

    Paraphrase: _____

    _____

Name _____ Date _____

Poetry Collection: Alfred, Lord Tennyson; Robert Browning; and Jean Toomer
Vocabulary Builder

Word List

millennial	slumbering	prow

A. DIRECTIONS: *Read the following sentences and fill in each blank with the most appropriate word from the list.*

1. The _____ boy did not hear his alarm clock ringing.
2. The _____ of the ship cut through the inky waves.
3. The _____ fears of computer failure in 2000 did not come to pass.

B. DIRECTIONS: *Follow the directions to write a sentence using each word.*

1. Use *millennial* in a sentence about an old castle.

   _____

   _____

2. Use *prow* in a sentence about a ship's figurehead.

   _____

   _____

3. Use *slumbering* in a sentence about hibernation.

   _____

   _____

C. DIRECTIONS: *Find the word or phrase that is most similar in meaning to the word in CAPITAL LETTERS. Circle the letter of your choice.*

1. SLUMBERING
   A. awakening
   B. imagining
   C. dreaming
   D. sleeping

2. MILLENNIAL
   A. in a great while
   B. of a hundred years
   C. of a thousand years
   D. every other year

3. PROW
   A. right
   B. front
   C. back
   D. left

Poetry Collection: Alfred, Lord Tennyson; Robert Browning; and Jean Toomer
Support for Writing a Poem

Before you begin to write your poem, fill in the following idea web with details you can include in your poem.

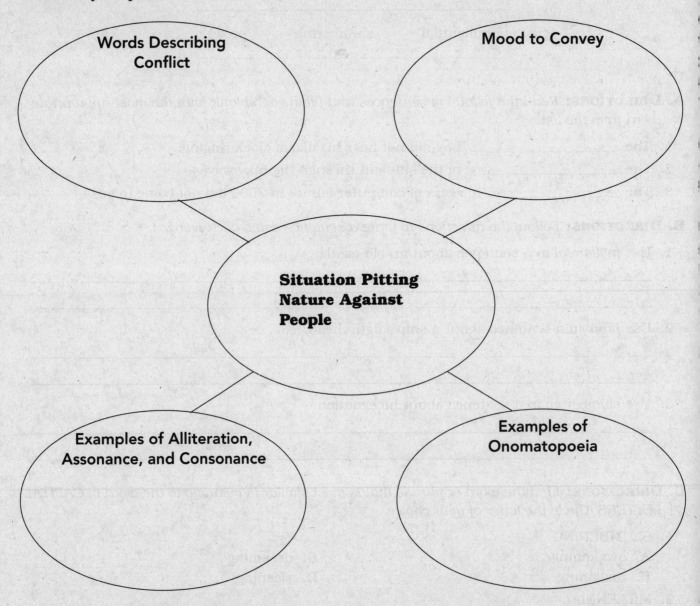

Now, use the details you have collected to write your poem that tells about a collision between nature and the world of people.

Poetry Collection: Alfred, Lord Tennyson; Robert Browning; and Jean Toomer
Support for Extend Your Learning

Listening and Speaking

On the following lines, write down the poets and poems you listened to. Then, write your reactions to the readings.

Poet 1: _____

Poems: _____

My reaction: _____

_____

Poet 2: _____

Poems: _____

My reaction: _____

_____

Poet 3: _____

Poems: _____

My reaction: _____

_____

Research and Technology

On the following lines, write the name of the artist and the artworks you have chosen to compare with Jean Toomer's poem. Then, list similarities and differences between the poem and the artworks.

Artist: _____

Works: _____

Similarities: _____

_____

Differences: _____

_____

Poetry Collection: Alfred, Lord Tennyson; Robert Browning; and Jean Toomer

Enrichment: Art and Poetry

While reading these poems, you may picture images of a lumbering sea monster, reapers moving scythes through a field, and a man pushing his boat onto a dark shore. Poets use descriptive words and phrases to create visual images for their readers.

A. DIRECTIONS: *In the following chart, record some of your favorite examples of visual imagery in the poems. List specific words and phrases.*

Poem	Visual Imagery
"The Kraken"	
"Meeting at Night"	
"Reapers"	

B. DIRECTIONS: *Illustrations and pieces of fine art can often complement images created by a poet. Think about what design you might create to accompany one of the poems in this collection. Use the images you listed on the chart to inspire your design. Then, create a sketch of your design.*

Poetry Collections: Langston Hughes; John McCrae; and Carl Sandburg;
Alfred, Lord Tennyson; Robert Browning; and Jean Toomer

Build Language Skills: Vocabulary Skill

Suffixes

Psychology attaches the **noun-forming** suffix *-logy*, which means "the science or study of," to the Greek word root *-psych-*, which means "soul or mind." *Psychology* is "the science or study of the human mind." *Drastic* adds the **adjective-forming** suffix *-ic*, which means "like or relating to," to the Greek word root *-drast-*, which means "action." *Drastic* means "relating to strong action" or "forceful; extreme."

A. DIRECTIONS: *Answer each question by using the italicized vocabulary word.*

1. If you studied *psychology*, would you learn about rocks and minerals?

   _____

2. If your friend is very *dramatic*, would she be likely to perform in a play?

   _____

3. Would a person who feels *civic* responsibility be inclined to run for mayor?

   _____

4. What would be the activity of someone whose field is *Egyptology*?

   _____

5. If you think a friend is behaving in an *idiotic* way, what should you do?

   _____

Academic Vocabulary Practice

distort	minimize	psychology	recur	drastic

B. DIRECTIONS: *Follow the instructions using the academic vocabulary words.*

1. Use *recur* in a sentence about a dream.

   _____

2. Use *minimize* in a sentence about tryouts for a play.

   _____

3. Use *distort* in a sentence about an argument.

   _____

4. Use *psychology* in a sentence about a book.

   _____

5. Use *drastic* in a sentence about a shopping trip.

   _____

Poetry Collections: Langston Hughes; John McCrae; and Carl Sandburg;
Alfred, Lord Tennyson; Robert Browning; and Jean Toomer

Build Language Skills: Grammar

Infinitives

An **infinitive** is a form of the verb that generally appears with the word *to* and acts as a noun, an adjective, or an adverb.

Infinitive as Noun: Last year Ana learned *to drive.* (direct object of *learned*)

Infinitive as Adjective: She had a great desire *to succeed.* (modifies *desire*)

Infinitive as Adverb: I am still unable *to drive.* (modifies *unable*)

An **infinitive phrase** consists of an infinitive along with any modifiers or complements, all acting together as a single part of speech.

Infinitive Phrase Containing a Modifier: He tried *to answer decisively.*

Infinitive Phrase Containing a Complement: No one is really able *to see the future.*

A. PRACTICE: *Underline the infinitive in each of the following sentences and indicate its function. Write* noun, adjective, *or* adverb *before the infinitive.*

_____ 1. Using a steady rhythm, Langston Hughes is able to re-create the feeling of the blues in "Weary Blues."

_____ 2. Carl Sandburg wanted to make his poem sound like the sounds of jazz music.

_____ 3. In "In Flanders Fields," the speakers wish their fight to continue.

_____ 4. To make a poem evocative often requires figurative language.

B. Writing Application: *Follow the directions in parentheses to write four sentences using infinitives and infinitive phrases.*

1. (Use the infinitive to *fight.*)

   _____

2. (Use the infinitive phrase *to play a musical instrument.*)

   _____

3. (Use the infinitive phrase *to sing the blues.*)

   _____

4. (Use the infinitive phrase *to rest in peace.*)

   _____

Poetry Collection: Alfred, Lord Tennyson; Robert Browning; and Jean Toomer
Selection Test A

Critical Reading *Identify the letter of the choice that best answers the question.*

____ 1. In "The Kraken," where can the Kraken be found?
   A. wandering through villages
   B. sleeping on a beach
   C. deep in the sea
   D. on the surface of the ocean

____ 2. In "The Kraken," when the Kraken is "Battening upon huge seaworms," what is it doing?
   A. lying beneath the seaworms
   B. playing with the seaworms
   C. struggling against the seaworms
   D. eating the seaworms

____ 3. Which of these phrases from "The Kraken" contains an example of assonance?
   A. "beneath in the abysmal sea"
   B. "Battening upon huge"
   C. "Then once by man"
   D. "he shall rise"

____ 4. Who or what is performing the action in these lines from "The Kraken"?
   Then once by man and angels to be seen, / In roaring he shall rise and on the surface die.
   A. Men
   B. angels
   C. the Kraken
   D. the speaker

____ 5. What is the speaker in "Meeting at Night" doing?
   A. sailing on the ocean
   B. going to meet his lover
   C. fishing in a lake
   D. finding his way home

____ 6. In "Meeting at Night," why are the waves "startled"?
   A. A storm has suddenly come up.
   B. The speaker is sailing through them.
   C. The moon has come out unexpectedly.
   D. The speaker has fallen out of his boat.

_____ 7. Which phrase from "Meeting at Night" contains alliteration?

    A. "the yellow half-moon large and low"

    B. "the two hearts beating each to each"

    C. "As I gain the cove"

    D. "Three fields to cross"

_____ 8. What action is taking place in these lines from "Meeting at Night"?

    As I gain the cove with pushing prow, / And quench its speed i' the slushy sand.

    A. The speaker is walking through the fields.

    B. The speaker is racing down the beach.

    C. The speaker is landing on the beach.

    D. The speaker's boat has overturned.

_____ 9. What word best describes the atmosphere of "Reapers"?

    A. grim

    B. matter-of-fact

    C. comical

    D. joyous

_____ 10. What happens to the field rat in "Reapers"?

    A. It is chased away by the reapers.

    B. It is taken in as a pet.

    C. It is frightened away by the horses.

    D. It is cut by the blade of a scythe.

_____ 11. What action is taking place in these lines from "Reapers"?

    I see them place the hones / In their hip-pockets as a thing that's done. . . .

    A. The reapers are sharpening their scythes.

    B. The reapers are driving the mower.

    C. The reapers are putting away their sharpeners.

    D. The reapers are swinging their scythes.

_____ 12. Which of the following phrases from "Reapers" contains an example of onomatopoeia?

    A. "In their hip-pockets"

    B. "horses drive a mower"

    C. "startled, squealing bleeds"

    D. "I see the blade"

Vocabulary and Grammar

___ 13. If Lindsey is slumbering, what is she doing?
   A. rumbling
   B. daydreaming
   C. waking
   D. sleeping

___ 14. Which of the following words is a synonym for *drastic*?
   A. encouraging
   B. bizarre
   C. reliable
   D. extreme

___ 15. Which words in the following sentence are an infinitive?
   The Kraken waits to surface at the end of time.
   A. The Kraken
   B. to surface
   C. at the end
   D. of time

Essay

16. In an essay, describe the experience of the speaker in "Meeting at Night." Paraphrase what happens in the poem. Where has the speaker been? What are his feelings on arriving at the farmhouse? What specific images convey the speaker's feelings throughout the poem?

17. "The Kraken," "Meeting at Night," and "Reapers" present a variety of vivid images. You can picture a frightening sea monster, a meeting at night, and a silent group of men working in a field. What image from these poems did you find most striking? Write an essay in which you describe the image and explain why you found it so effective.

Poetry Collection: Alfred, Lord Tennyson; Robert Browning; and Jean Toomer

Selection Test B

Critical Reading *Identify the letter of the choice that best completes the statement or answers the question.*

_____ 1. What sound device is shown by the italicized words in this passage from "The Kraken"?
Far, far *beneath* in the abysmal *sea*, / His ancient, *dreamless*, uninvaded *sleep*

    A. consonance
    B. assonance
    C. onomatopoeia
    D. alliteration

_____ 2. How could you best paraphrase these lines from "The Kraken"?
Then once by man and angels to be seen, / In roaring he shall rise and on the surface die.

    A. The Kraken will roar when he sees men and angels.
    B. The Kraken will battle men and angels and then die.
    C. The Kraken will awaken, rise, and die on the sea's surface.
    D. The Kraken will see men and angels once before he dies.

_____ 3. What sound device does Tennyson use in the following line from "The Kraken"?
Below the thunders of the upper deep

    A. consonance and alliteration
    B. onomatopoeia and assonance
    C. alliteration and onomatopoeia
    D. assonance and consonance

_____ 4. According to Tennyson's poem, what has the Kraken spent his time doing for ages?
    A. sleeping and eating huge seaworms
    B. attacking sailors
    C. rising to the surface of the ocean
    D. traveling throughout the ocean

_____ 5. On what type of journey has the speaker in "Meeting at Night" been?
    A. a spiritual journey
    B. a journey on horseback
    C. a journey at sea
    D. a mountain journey

_____ 6. What sound devices does Browning use in these lines from "Meeting at Night"?
The gray sea and the long black land; / And the yellow half-moon large and low

    A. onomatopoeia and assonance
    B. assonance and consonance
    C. alliteration and onomatopoeia
    D. alliteration and assonance

_____ 7. How can you paraphrase these lines from "Meeting at Night"?

As I gain the cove with pushing prow, / And quench its speed i' the slushy sand.

A. My boat is sinking in the sea.
B. I am landing the boat on the sand.
C. My boat is speeding across the sea.
D. I am swimming into the cove.

_____ 8. In the second verse of "Meeting at Night," where is the speaker going?
A. across the sea in a boat
B. along a beach on a walk
C. to a farmhouse to meet his beloved
D. to his death in the cold sea

_____ 9. What is the meaning of the following lines from "Meeting at Night"?

And a voice less loud, through its joys and fears, / Than the two hearts beating each to each!

A. The people are speechless, and the two hearts are beating with fear and anxiety.
B. The person at the door does not speak loudly enough to be heard over the ocean waves.
C. Voices cannot be heard over the couple's hearts, which are beating with love and happiness.
D. The two people meeting do not speak to each other.

_____ 10. What tone is created in the poem "Meeting at Night"?
A. a tone of terror and mystery
B. a tone of suspense and romance
C. a tone of sadness and loss
D. a tone of anxiety and fear

_____ 11. What is revealed by actions described in "Reapers"?
A. the numbing effect of repetitive work
B. the beauty of nature on a farm
C. how to operate a scythe effectively
D. the important role horses play at harvest time

_____ 12. What action is reflected by the repetition of sound in the following lines from "Reapers"?

Black reapers with the sound of steel on stones / Are sharpening scythes. I see them place the hones

A. the squeal of the field rat
B. the swish of the scythe blades
C. horses driving a mower through weeds
D. the setting of the sun on the farm

_____ 13. Which of these phrases from "Reapers" contains an example of consonance?
A. "belly close to ground"
B. "I see them place the hones"
C. "a field rat, startled"
D. "I see the blade"

____ 14. How could you paraphrase the following lines from "Reapers"?

> I see them place the hones / In their hip-pockets as a thing that's done, / And start their silent swinging, one by one.

A. The reapers begin to sharpen their scythes.
B. The reapers drive the mower through the weeds.
C. The reapers put their sharpeners in their pockets and start to cut.
D. The reapers swing their scythes and then stop to sharpen them.

Vocabulary and Grammar

____ 15. The monster in "The Kraken" is *slumbering* until the apocalypse. In other words, he is
A. dreaming.
B. sleeping.
C. eating.
D. waiting.

____ 16. The sponges in "The Kraken" are "of *millennial* growth." This means they have been growing for
A. a few years.
B. a hundred years.
C. a thousand years.
D. too many years to count.

____ 17. Someone who is studying *psychology* is learning about
A. the blood, organs, tissues, and muscles of the human body.
B. the way plants grow and reproduce.
C. the thought processes and emotional workings of the human mind.
D. the minerals and rocks of the earth.

____ 18. In which sentence is the infinitive used as a noun?
A. The speaker in "Meeting at Night" wants to meet his beloved.
B. The Kraken waits to emerge from the deep sea.
C. The lover waits for her beloved to arrive.
D. The reapers begin to cut the grass.

Essay

19. In both "The Kraken" and "Reapers," the poets use the alliterative sound of the letter *s* repeatedly. In an essay, explain how each poet uses the letter *s* and the effect of the repeated sound on the poem. Use details from the poems to support your conclusions.

20. "The Kraken" and "Meeting at Night" both tell a story. "The Kraken" is about a legendary beast, and "Meeting at Night" tells of a night journey. In an essay, use your own words to tell what happens in these poems. Refer back to words and phrases in the poems to clarify your paraphrasing.

Vocabulary Warm-up Word Lists

Study these words from the poetry of Dao, Ting, Dickinson, and Brontë. Then, apply your knowledge to the activities that follow.

Word List A

affection [uh FEK shuhn] *n.* a feeling of gentle love and caring
   Tim feels great <u>affection</u> for his cuddly little puppy.

disaster [di ZAS tuhr] *n.* a sudden event such as an accident, a flood, or a storm that causes great harm or damage
   The tsunami was the worst <u>disaster</u> of the century, with thousands dead.

encounter [en KOWN tuhr] *n.* an occasion when one meets or experiences something
   We may <u>encounter</u> some wildlife in the deep woods.

esteem [uh STEEM] *n.* a feeling of high regard and admiration
   Music critics hold Mozart's string quartets in high <u>esteem</u>.

fated [FAY tid] *adj.* certain to happen or to do something
   With so many shared interests, it was <u>fated</u> that we would meet some day.

liberty [LIB uhr tee] *n.* the freedom to do what you want without having to ask permission from people in authority
   The prisoner longed for the <u>liberty</u> to plan his daily activities and meals.

Word List B

barren [BAHR uhn] *adj.* unable to bring forth life
   Though the desert seemed <u>barren</u>, many plants and flowers grew there.

desolate [DES uh lit] *adj.* abandoned; empty
   It was hard to believe people had ever lived in the <u>desolate</u> ghost town.

implore [im PLAWR] *v.* to ask for something in an emotional way; to plead
   No matter how I <u>implore</u> them, my parents still will not let me travel alone.

repetition [re pi TI shuhn] *n.* the act of doing the same thing again and again
   Our <u>repetition</u> of the facts hundreds of times finally helped us learn them.

trodden [TRAHD n] *v.* having walked or stepped on something
   The children had <u>trodden</u> over the garden, ruining the flowerbeds.

vanished [VAN isht] *v.* having disappeared suddenly, especially in a way that cannot be easily explained
   We may never know exactly how the jewels <u>vanished</u> from the safe.

Poetry by Bei Dao, Shu Ting, Emily Dickinson, Emily Brontë
Vocabulary Warm-up Exercises

Exercise A *Fill in each blank in the paragraph with an appropriate word from Word List A. Use each word only once.*

When the leaders of the new nation broke away from their colonial rulers, they were seeking

[1] _____ and self-government. They knew that they would certainly

[2] _____ resistance in their quest for freedom. Though they held some of

their former rulers in high [3] _____, they felt no [4] _____ for

much of the royalty. In fact, when some of the independence-seekers tried to attack the royal

guard, they almost caused a major [5] _____. Thankfully, it was averted

through the quick thinking of the movement's leaders. From that point forward, it almost

seemed that a nonviolent road to independence had been [6] _____, as the

colony's rulers soon decided to relinquish their claim to rule without a struggle.

Exercise B *Revise each sentence so that the underlined vocabulary word is used in a logical way. Be sure to keep the vocabulary word in your revision.*

Example: It was easy to grow flowers and vegetables on the <u>barren</u> land.
It was difficult to grow anything on the <u>barren</u> land.

1. The <u>desolate</u> city was prosperous and booming.

   _____

2. I will only <u>implore</u> you to do something if I do not really care about the outcome.

   _____

3. We learned our lines by <u>repetition</u> after reciting them once.

   _____

4. The contractors had <u>trodden</u> over our vegetable garden, so we had a big harvest
   this year.

   _____

5. The rain <u>vanished</u> at noon, and it poured until nightfall.

   _____

Name _____ Date _____

Read the following passage. Pay special attention to the underlined words. Then, read it again, and complete the activities. Use a separate sheet of paper for your written answers.

The author of "The Old Stoic," a poem that glorifies liberty and freedom above all other things, was Emily Brontë, a member of the famous Brontë family of writers. Her sisters Charlotte and Anne both wrote popular books. Their only brother, Branwell, was said to have inspired some of their darker male characters.

Emily Brontë was the fifth child out of six. The family was touched by tragedy early, when Emily's mother died of tuberculosis. Emily's oldest sister, Maria, was only seven years old at the time. Three years later, sisters Maria, Elizabeth, Charlotte, and Emily went away to school. Sadly, disaster struck when Maria and Elizabeth both died of the disease that had killed their mother.

Emily and her siblings found solace in using their imaginations. They wrote plays and stories about a fantasyland of their own creation. Unfortunately, none of these early works survive.

The sisters' first encounter with publishing came when they wrote a collection of poems together. It was published under the names Acton (Anne), Ellis (Emily), and Currier (Charlotte) Bell. They used men's names so that their work would be taken seriously. This collection was not a commercial success.

The family's first successful work was Charlotte Brontë's *Jane Eyre*, a novel that is still held in high esteem today. In the same year, Emily published *Wuthering Heights*, but she did not live to see its popularity. Her novel of the tragic love between Catherine and Heathcliff is also considered a classic to this day. A year later, Anne Brontë published *The Tenant of Wildfell Hall*. None of these novels treats love as simple affection. In each of these books, the characters are tormented and overpowered by their emotions.

Sadly, each of the sisters was fated to die young—and each from tuberculosis. Branwell, the talented but troubled brother, also died young. The writings of the Brontës, however, will continue to live on.

1. Circle the synonym for liberty. Then, use *liberty* in a sentence.

2. Underline the phrase that tells what disaster struck the Brontë family. Explain what a *disaster* is.

3. Underline the phrase that describes the Brontë sisters' first encounter with publishing. Then, tell what *encounter* means.

4. Circle the words that tell which of Charlotte's books is still held in high esteem. Then, tell what *esteem* is.

5. Circle the word telling what is not treated as simple affection in the sisters' novels. Explain what *affection* is.

6. Underline the phrase that tells what each of the sisters was fated to do. Use *fated* in a sentence.

Poetry by Bei Dao, Shu Ting, Emily Dickinson, Emily Brontë
Reading Warm-up B

Read the following passage. Pay special attention to the underlined words. Then, read it again, and complete the activities. Use a separate sheet of paper for your written answers.

In the early 1800s, explorers roamed the world searching for adventure and riches. Our hero, Wen Dao, and his wife, Donglu were driven to find a certain ancient city described in legends. This city, supposedly in the middle of a barren desert in China, was said to be full of delicate, golden statues, beautiful buildings, and amazing artifacts. No one knew, though, exactly where to find it, as it was rumored to have vanished from the Earth.

First, Wen Dao tried to discover the whereabouts of the city by traveling to desolate regions and talking to people who retold legends about the city. He looked for clues in the stories themselves. Unfortunately, he got no closer to finding the city. Nevertheless, he was determined to keep searching.

Then, Donglu joined Wen Dao in his quest. Together they looked at ancient maps for evidence of a lost trade route. As they traveled, they found artifacts that had been trodden underfoot. These indicated that there must have been a rich civilization nearby, but again, Wen Dao and Donglu could not locate it. They were beginning to realize that they might not succeed in finding the city, and they became heartsick.

Finally, Wen Dao and Donglu decided to ask for aid, writing to their rulers, "We implore you to fund a full-scale expedition." Sadly, their request was denied.

They decided then to go back to their original clues. They asked people they had interviewed earlier to tell them their legends again. The repetition of these stories allowed them to focus on different details. Once again, they set out on their quest. They began their dig in a likely area. At last, they found evidence of a city! They were thrilled with their success, which they appreciated all the more after having failed in at first. They became famous throughout the world, and led many expeditions to the city of legend.

1. Why would it be surprising to find a city in a barren desert? Write an antonym for *barren*.

2. Underline the phrase that tells from where the city was rumored to have vanished. Then, tell what *vanished* means.

3. Would you expect to find many people in a desolate region? Tell why or why not. Write an antonym for *desolate*.

4. Circle the word that gives a clue to the meaning of trodden. If artifacts had been *trodden* over, would you expect them to be in perfect condition? Explain.

5. Underline the phrase that tells what the explorers would implore their rulers to do. Write about something you might *implore* someone to do. Use a synonym for the word in your answer.

6. Write a sentence about a lesson you have learned through repetition. Define *repetition* in your own words.

Name _____ Date _____

Poetry by Bei Dao, Shu Ting, Emily Dickinson, and Emily Brontë
Literary Analysis: Theme

A **theme** is the central idea, message, or insight that the author of a literary work conveys. Two poems might explore the same topic, but present very different themes. For example, one poem about the topic of failure might have the theme "A person must fail many times before he or she succeeds." Another poem about failure might have a very different theme, such as "Failing gracefully is a success in itself."

DIRECTIONS: *Answer the following questions to analyze each poem's unique theme.*

1. **A.** Identify two contradictions or conflicts the poet mentions in "All." _____

    _____

    _____

    B. Based on these contradictions, what do you think the poet is suggesting about human
    actions? _____

    _____

2. "Also All" was written in response to "All." In a sentence, summarize this response. _____

    _____

3. **A.** According to "Success is counted sweetest," who most appreciates the sweetness of
    success? _____

    B. How might you summarize this poem as a piece of advice? _____

    _____

    _____

4. **A.** In "The Old Stoic," Brontë explores a conflict between what is often counted as success
    and what the speaker counts as success. What "successes" does the speaker pray for?

    _____

    _____

    B. Do you agree or disagree with the speaker's insight about success? Why? _____

    _____

    _____

Name _____ Date _____

Poetry by Bei Dao, Shu Ting, Emily Dickinson, and Emily Brontë
Vocabulary Builder

Word List

| lamentation | wither | strains | implore |

A. DIRECTIONS: *Decide whether each statement is true or false. Explain your answers.*

1. If you water your tomato plants regularly, they will probably *wither*.

   _____

   _____

2. If you *implore* someone for a favor, it might be harder for the person to say no.

   _____

   _____

3. Great *lamentation* often follows a great victory.

   _____

   _____

4. A magnifying glass might aid you in detecting the *strains* of a bird.

   _____

   _____

B. DIRECTIONS: *On the line, write the letter of the word that is most similar in meaning to the word in CAPITAL LETTERS.*

____ 1. IMPLORE:
    A. burst   B. bend   C. beg   D. bake

____ 2. WITHER:
    A. shrivel   B. tremble   C. improve   D. endure

____ 3. LAMENTATION:
    A. excitement   B. uncertainty   C. performance   D. weeping

____ 4. STRAINS:
    A. deals   B. beliefs   C. tunes   D. statements

Poetry by Bei Dao, Shu Ting, Emily Dickinson, and Emily Brontë
Support for Writing to Compare Themes

Before you draft your essay comparing and contrasting the poets' ideas about hope and success, complete the following graphic organizer.

"All"	"Also All"
Poet's attitude:	Poet's attitude:
Supporting details:	Supporting details:

Hope and Success

"Success is counted sweetest"	"The Old Stoic"
Poet's attitude:	Poet's attitude:
Supporting details:	Supporting details:

Now, use your notes to write an essay comparing and contrasting the poets' ideas about people's hopes and their pursuit of success.

Name _____ Date _____

Poetry by Bei Dao, Shu Ting, Emily Dickinson, and Emily Brontë
Selection Test A

Critical Reading *Identify the letter of the choice that best answers the question.*

_____ 1. In "All," the speaker refers to "all love buried in the heart." What does he mean by this?
A. love that remains a secret
B. love that dies
C. love for someone who has died
D. love that is a mistake

_____ 2. What theme, or central idea, is expressed in "All"?
A. All grief will one day lead to joy.
B. Every experience in life is precious.
C. All speech is an expression of hatred.
D. Everything ends in despair and death.

_____ 3. Which sentence best expresses the theme of "Also All"?
A. Hope is a delusion of the weak and downtrodden.
B. We must be hopeful even when hope seems difficult.
C. There is no reason to hope, for we are doomed.
D. Those who have hope will live, while those without hope will die.

_____ 4. What is the meaning of the following lines from "Also All"?
   Not every song / will drift past every ear and heart.
A. Some songs will become "classics," while others will fade away.
B. Music will no longer be important to people in the future.
C. Some people will appreciate the world's beauty.
D. Many people will grow deaf and hateful.

_____ 5. What does the speaker in "Also All" believe about the future?
A. It will never arrive.
B. It is strongly connected to the present.
C. It cannot be shaped by the choices we make.
D. It will be identical to the past.

_____ 6. According to the speaker of "Success is counted sweetest," who most values success?
A. soldiers
B. people who love nature
C. unsuccessful people
D. poets

___ 7. In "Success is counted sweetest," what does the dying man represent?

    A. a person who longs for success

    B. a person who does not appreciate success

    C. a person who has achieved great success

    D. a person who has been afraid of success

___ 8. Which sentence best expresses the theme, or central insight, of "Success is counted sweetest"?

    A. Those who always succeed will finally die from it.

    B. Some people may never succeed, but they are still valuable.

    C. Some people succeed, but they do not realize it.

    D. Those who never succeed value success the most.

___ 9. In "The Old Stoic," what does the speaker value most highly?

    A. prayer

    B. liberty

    C. love

    D. art

___ 10. How does the speaker in "The Old Stoic" feel about riches, love, and fame?

    A. She desires them, but she knows she should not.

    B. She places no value in them.

    C. She thinks they are beautiful dreams.

    D. She believes they are evil.

___ 11. Which word best describes the speaker of "The Old Stoic"?

    A. outgoing

    B. happy

    C. independent

    D. vengeful

___ 12. Which poem presents the bleakest view of life?

    A. "All"

    B. "Also All"

    C. "Success is counted sweetest"

    D. "The Old Stoic"

____ 13. How does the poem "Also All" respond to the poem "All"?

A. It extends the poem with extra examples.

B. It disagrees with the poem's main idea.

C. It praises the poem's world view.

D. It answers the poem's questions.

____ 14. What might the speaker of "All" say to the speaker of "The Old Stoic"?

A. Death is only an illusion.

B. You should pray only for love.

C. You should try to avoid death.

D. It is useless to pray for anything.

Vocabulary

____ 15. In "Success is counted sweetest," the dying man hears the "distant strains of triumph." What are *strains*?

A. musical notes   C. whispers

B. blasts   D. shouts of joy

Essay

16. The poems "All," "Also All," "Success is counted sweetest," and "The Old Stoic" give a different answer to the question, "Do human actions and choices matter, and why?" Choose *three* of the four poems. Then, in a brief essay, explain how each poem answers this question.

17. In "The Old Stoic," the speaker longs for the "courage to endure." What might the speakers of "All" and "Also All" say about courage? Why might each speaker value or desire courage? Who might value it more? Answer these questions in a brief essay.

Poetry by Bei Dao, Shu Ting, Emily Dickinson, and Emily Brontë
Selection Test B

Critical Reading *Identify the letter of the choice that best completes the statement or answers the question.*

____ 1. In "All," what does the speaker mean when he says that "All is fated, / all cloudy"?
   A. that sunshine will come
   B. that humans choose stormy paths
   C. that it is possible to predict what will happen in the future
   D. that humans can do nothing to change a grim future

____ 2. Which word best describes the speaker's attitude toward life in "All"?
   A. resigned
   B. cautious
   C. jubilant
   D. fearful

____ 3. In "All," the speaker expresses the belief that all joy
   A. leads to greater joy.
   B. comes from love.
   C. will end in grief.
   D. is a gift to be treasured.

____ 4. In "Also All," the line "Today is heavy with tomorrow" means that
   A. our current troubles will cause us anxiety in the future.
   B. what happens today determines what happens tomorrow.
   C. both today and tomorrow are shrouded in doubt.
   D. today and tomorrow will be just the same.

____ 5. Which line from "Also All" best expresses the poem's theme, or central insight, about life?
   A. nor is all affection doomed. . . .
   B. No, not all is as you say.
   C. nor every soul be trodden under.
   D. Hope is a burden all of us shoulder. . . .

____ 6. With which statement would the author of "Also All" most likely agree?
   A. Some of life's moments are mournful, but others are joyful and hopeful.
   B. All of life's moments are joyful and hopeful.
   C. Life is one long, mournful experience.
   D. Life is filled with moments that are flat and meaningless.

____ 7. When Shu Ting writes that "not all is as you say," who is the "you"?
   A. the reader
   B. any hopeful person
   C. her elders
   D. another poet

____ 8. In "Success is counted sweetest," to what does the poet compare success?
A. losing a battle
B. contemplating nature
C. tasting a delicious drink
D. listening to a beautiful song

____ 9. For the dying man in "Success is counted sweetest," why do the "distant strains of triumph / Burst agonized and clear"?
A. He is having a supernatural experience.
B. Victory is the one thing he has most desired.
C. In death, he still loves music.
D. He feels defeated, afraid, and alone.

____ 10. What might the speaker of "Success is counted sweetest" say about those who *do* succeed?
A. that they do not fully appreciate their success
B. that they succeed because they are lucky
C. that their success is an illusion
D. that they are not worthy of success

____ 11. In "The Old Stoic," when the speaker seeks "a chainless soul," she means
A. she wishes to find someone who is her equal.
B. she wishes to be free of the cares of money.
C. she wishes her thoughts to be unrestricted.
D. she wishes to be free of her fame.

____ 12. Why does the speaker in "The Old Stoic" scorn wealth and fame?
A. She has experienced both, and she is now disillusioned.
B. She has grown bitter in her pursuit of them.
C. She strongly desires them, but she knows she should not.
D. She has learned that they are not as important as courage and liberty.

____ 13. What has prompted the speaker in "The Old Stoic" to shift her values?
A. the loss of a loved one
B. the nearness of death
C. an experience in nature
D. the advice of a friend

____ 14. Which poem expresses the message that it is utterly pointless to strive for success?
A. "All"
B. "Also All"
C. "Success is counted sweetest"
D. "The Old Stoic"

____ 15. How does the poem "Also All" relate to the poem "All"?
A. It is an attack on the poet of "All."
B. It is a tribute to the poet of "All."
C. It expresses an identical world view.
D. It expresses a very different world view.

_____ 16. Which poem expresses the idea that people's choices and actions do not matter?
    A. "All"
    B. "Success is counted sweetest"
    C. "Also All"
    D. "The Old Stoic"

_____ 17. With which idea might the poets of "All," "Also All," "Success is counted sweetest," and "The Old Stoic" all agree?
    A. True success is rare.
    B. It is useless to strive for success.
    C. Fame and fortune equal success.
    D. Anyone can achieve success.

_____ 18. What would the speaker of "The Old Stoic" most likely say in response to "Success is counted sweetest"?
    A. Military victories should not be considered true successes.
    B. Love is the sweetest success of all.
    C. Success can be attained only through prayer.
    D. Not everyone defines "success" in the same way.

Vocabulary

_____ 19. What does the word *lamentation* mean in the following passage from "All"?
    all hope hedged with doubt,
    all faith drowned in lamentation.
    A. awe   C. ecstasy
    B. grief   D. the ocean

_____ 20. If you *implore* your boss for a raise, you are
    A. demanding a raise.   C. pleading for a raise.
    B. thanking him or her for a raise.   D. hinting at a raise.

Essay

21. In their own ways, the poems "All," "Also All," "Success is counted sweetest," and "The Old Stoic" each express one of the following ideas: *Hope is essential* and *Hope is pointless*. In an essay, explain which poems express which idea, and how. In each poem, consider the specific application of each idea. For example, one poem might express the idea "Hope is essential to the attainment of a goal," while another may express the idea "Hope is pointless when death is near."

22. The poems in this group are all built upon a striking image or series of images. These images, in turn, help the poets express certain themes, or insights about life. For example, in "The Old Stoic," Brontë uses the image of a "chainless soul" to help express the theme that freedom and courage are the most precious riches in life. In an essay, identify a striking image in *two* of the other three poems—"All," "Also All," and "Success is counted sweetest"—and explain how each image helps the poet communicate an important insight.

23. "All," "Also All," "Success is counted sweetest," and "The Old Stoic" all describe or illustrate a basic conflict, contradiction, or paradox in life. Choose three of the four poems. Then, in an essay, identify the conflict each poem addresses. Do any of the poems offer a resolution for the conflict? Explain.

Name _____ Date _____

Analytic Response to Literature

Prewriting: Choosing Your Topic

Use the following chart to brainstorm about literary works that have provoked strong feelings in you. After you finish, review your list and choose one work as your topic.

Name of Literary Work	Author's Name	Memorable Details about the Work

Drafting: Shaping Your Writing

Organize your draft by using the graphic organizer below to list the details of your response.

Introduction (including Thesis Statement)	
Details of Body Paragraph 1	
Details of Body Paragraph 2	
Details of Body Paragraph 3	
Conclusion	

Writing Workshop—Unit 4, Part 2
Analytic Response to Literature: Integrating Grammar Skills

Revising Common Usage Problems: Making Comparisons

Words with similar meanings are often confused. Be careful to use the following words correctly in your writing.

- *Like,* which means "similar to" or "such as," is a preposition that connects a noun or pronoun to the rest of the sentence.
- *As* and *as if* are subordinating conjunctions that introduce clauses.
  Ms. Gray is tough but positive, just *as* she ought to be.
  She makes students feel *as if* they can succeed at anything.
- *Among,* a preposition, usually implies three or more.
- *Between,* also a preposition, is usually used only for just two things.
  The teaching awards were shared *among* four teachers.
  The Teacher of the Year award is *between* Ms. Gray and Mr. Lopez.

Identifying Correct Usage

A. DIRECTIONS: *Complete each sentence by circling the correct choice in parentheses.*

1. The Frick Museum is (between, among) the best art museums in New York City.
2. Frick divided his art collection (between, among) Pittsburgh and New York.
3. The Pittsburgh site is even more (like, as, as if) a stately home.
4. Rooms are restored to look just (like, as, as if) they looked decades ago.

Fixing Usage Problems

B. DIRECTIONS: *On the lines provided, rewrite these sentences so that they use the correct words.*

1. We watched the boat race among Rolf and Ian.

   _____

2. Rolf rowed like he had a lot of practice.

   _____

3. Both of them zipped along, just like I expected.

   _____

4. Between the dozens of other competitions, there was none as exciting.

   _____

Name _____ Date _____

Spelling Workshop—Unit 4
Words with Similar Endings

The **endings -yze, -ise, and -ize** can have similar pronunciations that lead to confusion about spelling. Both *-ise* and *-ize* can be pronounced "īz." Since words with these endings provide no sound clues, you need to memorize the spelling of any word that causes you problems.

Word List

supervise	plagiarize	improvise	paradise	paralyze
exercise	disguise	jeopardize	commercialize	treatise

A. DIRECTIONS: *Write the word in parentheses that is correctly spelled.*

1. wore an elaborate (disguise, duisgize)   _____
2. the teacher (supervised, supervised) the students   _____
3. a vacation in a real (paradise, paradice)   _____
4. it is illegal to (plagiarize, plagiarise)   _____
5. a boring (treatice, treatise) about bacteria   _____
6. could (improvise, improvize) a new ending   _____
7. might (jepardise, jeopardize) the crew's safety   _____
8. (paralyzed, paralyzed) with fear   _____
9. (exersize, exercise) is good for the body   _____
10. to (commercialize, commercialise) the holiday   _____

B. DIRECTIONS: *Choose two phrases that you corrected above. Write a brief paragraph based on each one. Use at least three other list words in each paragraph.*

1. phrase: _____
   _____
   _____
   _____

2. phrase: _____
   _____
   _____
   _____

Name _____ Date _____

Communications Workshop—Unit 4
Delivering an Oral Interpretation of a Literary Work

Select a poem, short story, or short piece of nonfiction to use in a three-minute interpretation. Use the following chart to help you organize your interpretation.

Title of poem, short story, or piece of nonfiction: _____

What is the main idea of the piece?
What details support this main idea?
What quotations will you include?
What subtleties will you explain from the text?
How will you organize your interpretation?
What gestures or body language will you use?

For Further Reading—Unit 4

DIRECTIONS: *Think about the books you have read. Then, on a separate sheet of paper, answer the discussion questions and take notes for your literature circle.*

Beowulf

Discussion Beowulf was a hero in his society. Define the characteristics that made him a hero. Use specific examples from the text to demonstrate your points.

Connections—Literature Circle Develop a definition of our society's concept of a hero. If Beowulf lived today, how would his characteristics have to change?

Song of a Lark by Willa Cather

Discussion "Art, it seems to me, should simplify finding what conventions of form and what detail one can do without and yet preserve the spirit of the whole—so that all that one has suppressed and cut away is there to the reader's consciousness as much as if it were in type on the page." According to her own definition, has Cather succeeded in creating "art" in *The Song of a Lark*? Explain.

Connections—Literature Circle How does the environment surrounding an artist influence his or her work? Formulate a theory of art and the impact of environmental influences using examples from *Song of a Lark* and your own knowledge to demonstrate why your theory makes sense.

Native American Literature from Prentice Hall Literature Library

Discussion Evaluate three selections in this anthology. How do the topics lead you to an understanding of what was valued in Native American culture?

Connections—Literature Circle Most Native American myths and legends were spoken, not written down. How does this oral tradition translate to the written form? What do you think is lost when a storyteller is not involved in these stories? What do you think is gained?

Leaves of Grass by Walt Whitman

Discussion "Indeed his independence often becomes coarse and defiant. His language is too frequently reckless and indecent though this appears to arise from a naïve unconsciousness rather than from an impure mind." —Charles A. Dana, (New York Daily Tribune, 23 July 1855) This is a literary critic's view of *Leaves of Grass*. Contemporary critics generally consider Whitman a great American poet. Based on your reading of the poems, judge which group is correct.

Connection—Literature Circle Whitman's poetry was considered shocking in its time. Compare this poetry to current music lyrics that an older generation considers "coarse and defiant." Use specifics from the poems to establish your comparison.

Unit 4: Poetry
Part 2 Benchmark Test 8

MULTIPLE CHOICE

Reading Skill *Picture the imagery as you read Trumbull Stickney's "I Hear a River Thro' the Valley Wander." Then, answer the three questions that follow.*

> I hear a river thro' the valley wander
> Whose water runs, the song alone remaining.
> A rainbow stands and summer passes under.

1. Who or what performs the main actions of the poem?
   A. The river wanders and sings.
   B. The valley wanders and runs.
   C. The speaker hears and sings.
   D. The rainbow stands and passes.

2. Which choice is the best paraphrase of the poem?
   A. As I wander through a valley, I hear the running waters of a river. I sing as a beautiful summer rainbow appears.
   B. Whose water do I hear running as I wander through the valley on a river? It is summertime, and a rainbow appears.
   C. I hear a river and it fills me with song. I am a wanderer, alone in a valley. A rainbow appears, but summer passes quickly.
   D. As a river wanders though a valley, I hear the music of running water. A rainbow arches over the summer scene.

Read the selection from Rupert Brooke's "Seaside," and answer the questions.

> Swiftly out from the friendly lilt of the band,
> The crowd's good laughter, the loved eyes of men,
> I am drawn nightward; I must turn again
> Where, down beyond the low untrodden strand,
> 5 There curves and glimmers outward to the unknown
> The old unquiet ocean. All the shade
> Is rife with magic and movement. I stray alone
> Here on the edge of silence, half afraid, [. . .]

3. In lines 1 through 3, up to the semicolon, what is the main action?
   A. the friendly lilt
   B. the crowd's good laughter
   C. the loved eyes of men
   D. I am drawn

4. What is the main idea in lines 3 through 5?
   A. I must turn to the old unquiet ocean.
   B. I will be the first to walk on the strand.
   C. The ocean curves and glimmers.
   D. I must do what I did before.

5. Which image might you picture to paraphrase this stanza of the poem?
   A. a concert on an ocean liner sailing into the night
   B. the ocean sparkling in the noon sun
   C. a man turning away from a party to walk towards the sea at night
   D. a man surrounded by his friends, having a good time on the beach

6. Which of these is typical of a feature article in a newspaper or magazine?
   A. It focuses on an event, activity, or trend, not on a person or place.
   B. It has a central "angle" or theme that the writer elaborates.
   C. It presents one person's opinions with no backup from experts or participants.
   D. It does not include graphics such as photographs, maps, or charts.

7. Which of the following does this sentence represent?

   The author fails to recognize that his argument is undermined by the existence of other interpretations of the work, which are just as valid.

   A. a quotation
   B. a paraphrase
   C. a critique
   D. a summary

8. What is wrong with this sentence from someone's notes?

   According to a famous poet, "Stone walls do not a prison make."

   A. It should use a colon, not a comma, before the quotation.
   B. It should use other words to restate the material in quotation marks.
   C. It should not use quotation marks.
   D. It should give the name of the famous poet.

Literary Analysis

9. What is an analogy?
   A. a comparison of two things that are alike in some respects but not others
   B. a quotation that an author cites at the start of a work or a section of a work
   C. a group of letters that can be unscrambled to spell a word or phrase
   D. an abbreviation formed from the first letters of several words

Name _____ Date _____

Read the selection from John Masefield's "Sea-Fever," and answer the questions.

> I must down to the seas again, to the lonely sea and the sky,
> And all I ask is a tall ship and a star to steer her by,
> And the wheel's kick and the wind's song and the white sail's shaking,
> And a grey mist on the sea's face and a grey dawn breaking.
>
> [. . .]
>
> 5 I must down to the seas again, to the vagrant gypsy life,
> To the gull's way and the whale's way, where the wind's like a whetted knife;
> And all I ask is a merry yarn from a laughing fellow-rover,
> And quiet sleep and a sweet dream when the long trick's over.

10. Which of these is the best example of alliteration?
   A. *all* and *tall* in line 2
   B. *ship, star,* and *steer* in line 2
   C. *wheel's, wind's,* and *white* in line 3
   D. *grey* and *breaking* in line 4

11. Which of these is the best example of assonance?
   A. *down, again,* and *lonely* in line 1
   B. *star* and *steer* in line 2
   C. *wheel's kick* in line 3
   D. *sail's shaking* in line 3

12. What simile occurs in the last stanza?
   A. The speaker compares a life at sea to that of a vagrant, or wandering, gypsy.
   B. The speaker calls a life at sea "the gull's way" and "the whale's way."
   C. The speaker describes wind "like a whetted knife" on the sea.
   D. The speaker describes a yarn, or tall tale, as "merry."

Read the selection from Sara Teasdale's "Open Windows," and answer the questions.

> [. . .]
> I am alone with Weakness and Pain,
> Sick abed and June is going,
> I cannot keep her, she hurries by
> With the silver-green of her garments blowing.
>
> 5 Men and women pass in the street
> Glad of the shining sapphire weather,
> But we know more of it than they,
> Pain and I together.
>
> They are the runners in the sun,
> 10 Breathless and blinded by the race,
> But we are the watchers in the shade
> Who speak with Wonder face to face.

13. What is personified in lines 3 through 4?
    A. Weakness
    B. Pain
    C. June
    D. the speaker

14. What metaphors does the final stanza use?
    A. It compares those outside to runners in the sun and the speaker and Pain to those watching the runners from the shade.
    B. It compares Weakness and Pain to runners in the sun and compares the speaker to those watching the runners from the shade.
    C. It compares the speaker and Pain to runners in the sun and those outside to those watching the runners from the shade.
    D. It compares June to runners in the sun and compares the speaker's inability to enjoy June to runners who must watch a race from the shade.

15. Given your interpretation of the figurative language, what is the theme of the poem
    A. People who do not get enough exercise will often fall ill.
    B. Illness in good weather is particularly miserable.
    C. Those who suffer pain without complaint grow stronger, not weaker.
    D. Sometimes illness gives people a sharper appreciation of everyday life.

Read the selection from Eleanor Wylie's "Pretty Words," and answer the questions.

> Poets make pets of pretty, docile words:
> I love smooth words, like gold-enamelled fish
> Which circle slowly with a silken swish,
> And tender ones, like downy-feathered birds:
> 5 Words shy and dappled, deep-eyed deer in herds,
> Come to my hand, and playful if I wish,
> Or purring softly at a silver dish,
> Blue Persian kittens fed on cream and curds.

16. Which sound in line 1 is repeated in an example of consonance?
    A. the *p* sound
    B. the *ts* sound
    C. the long *a* sound
    D. the *k* sound

17. Which words in the poem are the clearest examples of onomatopoeia?
    A. *swish* and *purring*
    B. *dappled* and *softly*
    C. *docile* and *tender*
    D. *silver* and *dish*

18. How is the figure of speech in line 5 different from the figures of speech in lines 2 and 4?
   A. It is a metaphor, not a simile.
   B. It is a simile, not a metaphor.
   C. It involves personification; the others do not.
   D. It involves animals; the others do not.

Vocabulary

19. What part of speech does the suffix *-ize* form?
   A. nouns
   B. verbs
   C. adjectives
   D. adverbs

20. Which sentence uses the italicized word correctly?
   A. You need to *minimize* the problem, not make it smaller.
   B. In just a short *minimize*, the bell will ring.
   C. We need to *maximize* use of our resources.
   D. Will you *maximize* her wise words into a proverb?

21. The Greek root *-astro-* means "star." Knowing that, what can you conclude about *astrology*?
   A. Astrology probably involves the study of heavenly bodies.
   B. Astrology probably involves painting the stars.
   C. Astrology probably involves acting and the theater.
   D. Astrology probably requires deep understanding of human behavior.

Grammar

22. What is the prepositional phrase in this sentence, and what does it modify?

   The purpose of the last song was to show off all the musicians' talents.

   A. *of the last song*; an adjective phrase that modifies the noun *purpose*
   B. *to show off all the musicians' talents*; an adverb phrase that modifies the verb *was*
   C. *to show off*; an adjective phrase that modifies the noun *talents*
   D. *off the musicians' talents*; an adverb phrase that modifies the verb *show*

23. What is the infinitive phrase in this sentence?

   In August, we went to Ontario and to upstate New York to see Niagara Falls.

   A. to Ontario
   B. to upstate New York
   C. to see
   D. to see Niagara Falls

24. Which of these sentences contains an infinitive phrase that serves as a noun?
    A. Margo traveled to Oregon to visit her aunt and uncle.
    B. Her desire to see her ailing relatives was very strong.
    C. With the whole summer off, she decided to go by train.
    D. She used her computer to buy her ticket on line.

25. In the following sentence, what role does the italic infinitive phrase serve and what is its relationship to the other words in the sentence?

    The politician was driven by a need *to please others.*

    A. It serves as a noun, functioning as the direct object of the verb *was driven.*
    B. It serves as a noun, functioning as the object of the preposition *by.*
    C. It serves as an adjective, modifying the noun *need.*
    D. It serves as an adverb, modifying the verb *was driven.*

26. Which sentence has no problems in usage?
    A. Sonia felt like she was the best swimmer in the world.
    B. It was so hot, the pool felt as a warm bath.
    C. When she jumped in, it seemed like a bird was diving into the water.
    D. She paddled around as if she had all the time in the world.

Spelling

27. Which word is spelled correctly?
    A. compromize
    B. hypothesyze
    C. analize
    D. memorize

28. In which sentence is the italic word spelled correctly?
    A. The new company offers a fine line of *merchandize.*
    B. As new sellers, they need to *advertize* their product.
    C. Once they *publicize* what they offer, people will buy it.
    D. The company name should come to *symbolise* quality.

ESSAY

29. Think of a song for which you know all the words. Then, write a critical essay explaining why you do or do not like the song.

30. Write a poem about something that made a strong impression on you. The experience could be one that was either pleasant or unpleasant. Use strong, precise images in your poem, as well as figurative language and sound devices.

31. Think of a book you have read that left a strong impression on you. It might be a book you really loved or one that made you very angry or unhappy. Write a brief analytic response to the book with a strong thesis statement and examples that illustrate your main point.

ANSWERS

The Poetry of Cornelius Eady
Cornelius Eady

Vocabulary Warm-up Exercises, p. 2

A. 1. renowned
2. slight
3. uncouple
4. principles
5. sympathy
6. equivalent

B. Sample Answers
1. You will be quite surprised if your *expectation* is proven wrong.
2. A bicycle is a *practical* way to get to school.
3. One *application* of a calculator is adding expenses.
4. I knew the room was a *laboratory* because I saw a lot of test tubes and chemicals.
5. A basketball sitting motionless on the floor is an example of *inertia*.

Reading Warm-up A, p. 3

Sample Answers
1. (rules); *Principles* are the basic rules, laws, or ideas behind something.
2. taking a few steps apart to twist the night away; A driver might *uncouple* a trailer from a car.
3. the invention of the car in the world of transportation; *Equivalent* means "equal to."
4. It re-entered the music charts and quickly regained the top position. Elvis Presley is a *renowned* singer today even though he is no longer alive.
5. his other abilities; *Slight* means to "ignore or treat as unimportant."
6. (felt jealousy); I would feel *sympathy* for someone whose pet was sick.

Reading Warm-up B, p. 4

Sample Answers
1. (mice) (test tubes) (white coat); A *laboratory* is cold and unfriendly, so it would not be a fun place to dance.
2. (stuck in one place); *Inertia* is the tendency of an object to stay at rest unless something makes it start to move.
3. you and your friends will soon be dancing until you drop; *Application* means "the use of something."
4. Let everyone know that your party will include dancing. It was my *expectation* that I would get a B on the test, and I did.
5. Make sure you have enough room to dance. If you are new to school, it would be *practical* to make a list of names to help you remember people.
6. A good mix of music; I think that the *foundation* of a good dance song is a steady beat.

Listening and Viewing, p. 5

Sample Answers

Segment 1. Students should recognize that Eady discovered that jazz solos tell a story about the soloist, and that realization allowed him to write poems that, like jazz riffs, told stories about him, other people, culture, and history. Students should point to features of poetry that lend themselves to self-expression; for example, poetry allows for both the concise expression of ideas and the use of language with multiple layers of meaning.

Segment 2. Students should note that Eady uses repetition in his poetry to create rhythm; they might suggest that Eady hopes to create a musical beat, a sense of energy, or a sense of movement that will make an impression on the reader.

Segment 3. Students should note that Eady reads his poems aloud to hear how they sound and to make sure they are lively and "working" the way he wants them to. Students should express the idea that reading a poem aloud adds sound to the poem and may help the reader or writer recognize additional layers of meaning in it.

Segment 4. Students should note that Eady hopes his readers will be entertained, discover new things, and "enter the world" he writes about. In their statements about why writing stories about themselves is important, students should describe a benefit that writing has for the writer, the reader, or both. For example, they might suggest that it is important to share stories with others because in the process of telling stories, a writer can discover more about himself or herself and help readers recognize certain things that many people have in common.

Learning About Poetry, p. 6

A. 1. metaphor
2. rhythm
3. epic
4. free verse
5. rhyme
6. personification
7. imagery
8. sonnet

B. It is a haiku. It uses imagery (*blanket* appeals to the sense of sight; *no warmth* appeals to the sense of touch), metaphor (the snow is described as a blanket), and alliteration (*blanket bringing; warmth / Winter*).

The Poetry of Cornelius Eady

Model Selection: Poetry, p. 7

Sample Answers
A. *Simile:* In "The Poetic Interpretation of the Twist," the speaker describes his sister as "running like a giraffe." Note: A less obvious simile is the speaker's comparison

of his recalling the twist to the way an adult recalls meeting a distant relative when he or she—the adult— was a baby and of the feeling of waiting in homeroom for the last bell of the day to ring. In "The Empty Dance Shoes," the speaker uses many similes, comparing the shoe sitting on the floor to a wart; the energy of the shoes at rest to "a clown / Knocked flat by a sandbag"; and the empty shoes to a leaf pressed between the pages of a book, a rock that has settled in the mud at the bottom of a lake, the answer to the question "Whose Turn Is It / To Take Out the Garbage?," "book-length poems / set in the Midwest," and a weakling whose girl-friend has been stolen by a bully.

Metaphor: In "The Poetic Interpretation of the Twist," the speaker uses several metaphors to describe the twist: It is "the high sign / In a secret cult," a child's game, and "the foundation of a bridge / That has made way for a housing project." He also uses a metaphor to compare ragweed to "the true rose of the street," to compare the question about the twist to a burden ("a troublesome responsibility") placed on his shoulders, and to compare the feeling of not quite remembering many things to the feeling of having "the world on the tip of my tongue." Note: The last two metaphors exemplify the fact that many common idioms are rooted in metaphor.

Personification: The speaker of "The Empty Dance Shoes" personifies the shoes in several instances: They "sit" on the floor, they "run on their own sense of the world," and they feel sympathy.

B. Students should draw three inferences about the speaker. The inferences may be simple—for example, the speaker was growing up when the twist was popular; he thinks of his childhood neighborhood as a dead-end street next to railroad tracks; his sister was a fast, perhaps untamed runner; his father rode a bicycle; and so on. Alternatively, the inferences may be more complex—for example, deal-ing with how the speaker cannot explain the twist and claims to be confused by many aspects of the era, how he speaks of his family and his neighborhood instead of answering the question about the twist, and how the pro-cess of remembering makes him feel tired.

Selection Test A, p. 8

Critical Thinking

1. ANS: B	DIF: Easy	OBJ: Literary Analysis
2. ANS: A	DIF: Easy	OBJ: Literary Analysis
3. ANS: C	DIF: Easy	OBJ: Literary Analysis
4. ANS: B	DIF: Easy	OBJ: Literary Analysis
5. ANS: A	DIF: Easy	OBJ: Literary Analysis

Critical Reading

6. ANS: B	DIF: Easy	OBJ: Comprehension
7. ANS: C	DIF: Easy	OBJ: Comprehension
8. ANS: A	DIF: Easy	OBJ: Interpretation

9. ANS: C	DIF: Easy	OBJ: Literary Analysis
10. ANS: A	DIF: Easy	OBJ: Comprehension
11. ANS: B	DIF: Easy	OBJ: Comprehension
12. ANS: A	DIF: Easy	OBJ: Interpretation
13. ANS: A	DIF: Easy	OBJ: Literary Analysis
14. ANS: C	DIF: Easy	OBJ: Comprehension
15. ANS: D	DIF: Easy	OBJ: Interpretation

Essay

16. Students should recognize that thinking about the twist leads the speaker to various recollections of his child-hood. They might mention the mini-skirt, "the deep meaning of vinyl on everything," the way his sister ran, the location of his street, his father on a bicycle, and so on. They may also recognize that the speaker's recollec-tions lead him to think about how the world has changed, how vague his memory of the dance is, and how difficult it is to remember the dance clearly.

Difficulty: *Easy*

Objective: *Essay*

17. Students should note that all of the objects to which the shoes are compared are lying still; most of them once moved but have stopped moving, and some, such as the clown, will move again. The effect is to emphasize that the shoes are not moving and to suggest that they may have moved recently and may move—or dance—again.

Difficulty: *Easy*

Objective: *Essay*

Selection Test B, p. 11

Critical Thinking

1. ANS: B	DIF: Challenging	OBJ: Literary Analysis
2. ANS: B	DIF: Average	OBJ: Literary Analysis
3. ANS: B	DIF: Average	OBJ: Literary Analysis
4. ANS: B	DIF: Average	OBJ: Literary Analysis
5. ANS: D	DIF: Average	OBJ: Literary Analysis
6. ANS: A	DIF: Average	OBJ: Literary Analysis

Critical Reading

7. ANS: A	DIF: Average	OBJ: Comprehension
8. ANS: B	DIF: Average	OBJ: Interpretation
9. ANS: D	DIF: Average	OBJ: Comprehension
10. ANS: C	DIF: Average	OBJ: Interpretation
11. ANS: C	DIF: Average	OBJ: Literary Analysis
12. ANS: C	DIF: Average	OBJ: Comprehension
13. ANS: A	DIF: Challenging	OBJ: Interpretation
14. ANS: B	DIF: Challenging	OBJ: Literary Analysis
15. ANS: A	DIF: Challenging	OBJ: Interpretation
16. ANS: D	DIF: Challenging	OBJ: Interpretation

17. ANS: B	DIF: Average	OBJ: Literary Analysis
18. ANS: C	DIF: Average	OBJ: Comprehension
19. ANS: A	DIF: Challenging	OBJ: Interpretation
20. ANS: C	DIF: Average	OBJ: Literary Analysis

| 13. ANS: B |
| 14. ANS: C |
| 15. ANS: B |

Essay

21. Students should realize that at the end of the poem, the "98-pound weakling" whose girlfriend has been stolen by a "bully" "is ready to dance," thus defying the idea that a body at rest will remain at rest.

    Difficulty: *Average*

    Objective: *Essay*

22. Students should recognize that the speaker is saying that the twist laid the foundations for something that was in effect a bridge to something like a housing project. They might note that a bridge is a connection to something else; it often symbolizes improved circumstances. Here, however, the bridge leads to a housing project, which symbolizes negative things, such as dreariness and perhaps poverty and even crime. Perceptive students may interpret the statement to mean that the dreams and freedom implied by the twist were replaced by an unimaginative structure.

    Difficulty: *Average*

    Objective: *Essay*

23. Students should state some relevant question, such as, How did the twist reflect the era of the 1960s and your own experience of that time? They may suggest that the expectation it raises is the speaker's ability to explain the significance of the twist in terms of the society of the time. He finds it troublesome that he feels unable to act like a teacher, explaining the meaning of his era to a younger generation.

    Difficulty: *Challenging*

    Objective: *Essay*

Unit 4, Part 1 Answers

Diagnostic Test 7, p. 15

MULTIPLE CHOICE

1. ANS: B
2. ANS: A
3. ANS: A
4. ANS: D
5. ANS: C
6. ANS: A
7. ANS: D
8. ANS: B
9. ANS: B
10. ANS: D
11. ANS: A
12. ANS: C

Poetry Collection: Alexander Pushkin, Federico García Lorca, Elizabeth Bishop, and Rudyard Kipling

Vocabulary Warm-up Exercises, p. 19

A.
1. fast
2. whimpers
3. seize
4. headlong
5. battered
6. mourns

B. Sample Answers
1. T; A buyer might need to fumigate a house <u>infested</u> with termites, making it less appealing.
2. F; A lot of <u>tumult</u> would make it difficult to sleep.
3. F; Although it can be difficult, a <u>tarnished</u> reputation can be improved by a long period of good behavior.
4. T; A <u>regiment</u> includes many military personnel and would require many resources to be fed.
5. T; The sky's <u>vaults</u> usually cover with clouds and grow darker during a storm.
6. T; Waking up on another planet would be extremely confusing, so being <u>distraught</u> would be a natural reaction.

Reading Warm-up A, p. 20

Sample Answers
1. <u>a soft cry that sounds shy and afraid</u>; *Whimpers* means "cries in a soft way."
2. <u>bent in several places and very rusty</u>; *Battered* means "beaten up."
3. <u>its leg</u>; When something is held *fast*, it means it is "tightly grasped," as in this context; it does not mean "speedy."
4. (the grill); If you *seize* a wild animal, it might attack you.
5. Someone making a *headlong* dash is in an uncontrolled hurry, leading with his or her head.
6. (the lost raccoon); When someone *mourns*, he or she looks sad and cries.

Reading Warm-up B, p. 21

Sample Answers
1. (extreme noise and confusion); I was in a *tumult* on the first day of camp last summer when the luggage cart rolled into the lake.
2. <u>the difficult conditions they experience</u>; *Distraught* means "very upset or troubled."
3. (forks); A silver vase could also be *tarnished* if it is not polished regularly.

4. (fleas) (lice) (other bugs); *Infested* means "overrun with."

5. (soldiers); You might find a *regiment* at a military school or at a war front.

6. of a foreign sky; *Vaults* means "arched spaces; the arches of the sky"

Poetry Collection: Alexander Pushkin, Federico García Lorca, Elizabeth Bishop, and Rudyard Kipling

Literary Analysis: Narrative and Lyric Poetry, p. 22

1. It is a narrative poem because it begins by describing the actions of a character named Natasha. It tells a story.

2. Imagery: "It weeps" and "White camellias" appeal to the sense of sight. "Warm southern sands" appeals to the sense of touch. The lines create a feeling of sadness and yearning.

3. The medals suggest that the speaker sees the fish as a sort of war hero. She admires the fish's cleverness in escaping five times. She feels compassion for the fish's "aching jaw."

4. The character Files-on-Parade asks questions. The Color-Sergeant's answers describe the setting and tell the story of Danny Deever's hanging.

Reading: Read Aloud and Adjust Reading Rate to Read Fluently, p. 23

1. A. The lines contain one complete sentence;
   B. Readers should pause briefly after the words *pie* and *riddles*.

2. The exclamation point causes the reader to pause and give greater emphasis to the line. It shows that the line should be read with great emotion.

3. A. Students should underline the adjectives *battered*, *venerable*, and *homely*.
   B. Students should bracket [Here and there] [his brown skin] [hung in strips] [like ancient wallpaper,].

4. The quotation marks identify when each character is speaking. The words in quotation marks should be read in a different tone of voice from those that are not in quotation marks. The question marks cue the reader to read the lines as questions.

Vocabulary Builder, p. 24

A. Sample Answers

1. I might have a feeling of foreboding if I hadn't studied and knew I wasn't going to do well.

2. I would feel bored and restless.

3. I would treat the visitor with great respect.

4. The army airs TV commercials describing the benefits of enlisting.

B. 1. B; 2. C; 3. D

Enrichment: Random Acts of Kindness, p. 27

Suggested responses:

Caution students about choosing acts that might be viewed as intrusive by the recipients or beneficiaries. Remind students that random acts of kindness should not be used to show off or demonstrate one's abilities. Students' acts might best be performed for classmates or family members, rather than for neighbors or strangers.

Responses to the acts may range from surprised delight to a simple nod of the head. If students encounter anger or rejection, help them understand why the nature of the act or the circumstances might have elicited such a response. Help students to see that negative responses are not a reason to stop performing random acts of kindness.

Some students might report feeling awkward while doing something nice or offering to help someone. Ask students to focus on how they felt after the act of kindness, not during it. Students' responses may be no more specific than "It felt good." Use class discussion to investigate why it felt good. Help students discover, if necessary, that it is human nature to like being helpful and to "feel good" simply because one has made someone else feel good.

Selection Test A, p. 28

Critical Reading

1. ANS: B	DIF: Easy	OBJ: Literary Analysis
2. ANS: C	DIF: Easy	OBJ: Comprehension
3. ANS: A	DIF: Easy	OBJ: Interpretation
4. ANS: C	DIF: Easy	OBJ: Literary Analysis
5. ANS: D	DIF: Easy	OBJ: Reading Strategy
6. ANS: B	DIF: Easy	OBJ: Interpretation
7. ANS: C	DIF: Easy	OBJ: Comprehension
8. ANS: B	DIF: Easy	OBJ: Reading Strategy
9. ANS: A	DIF: Easy	OBJ: Literary Analysis
10. ANS: D	DIF: Easy	OBJ: Comprehension
11. ANS: A	DIF: Easy	OBJ: Interpretation
12. ANS: D	DIF: Easy	OBJ: Interpretation

Vocabulary and Grammar

13. ANS: B	DIF: Easy	OBJ: Vocabulary
14. ANS: A	DIF: Easy	OBJ: Vocabulary
15. ANS: C	DIF: Easy	OBJ: Grammar

Essay

16. Students may summarize the story told in "The Bridegroom," "The Fish," or "Danny Deever." "The Bridegroom" is set in Russia long ago, when parents still arranged marriages for their children. The main characters are Natasha, the bridegroom, the matchmaker, and Natasha's parents. Students should summarize the main events that lead to the bridegroom's being arrested by the police

after Natasha describes her "dream." "The Fish" is set on a boat on a lake in the present day. The only character is the woman who catches the fish. Students should describe what the woman sees when she catches the fish and why she decides to let it go. "Danny Deever" is set at a British army camp in the late 1800s. Through the dialogue of its two characters, Files-on-Parade and the Color-Sergeant, readers learn that a young soldier named Danny Deever, a friend of Files-on-Parade, is about to be hung for committing an unnamed crime.

Difficulty: *Easy*

Objective: *Essay*

17. Students should accurately describe the emotional impact of one of the four poems. They should cite descriptions, events, or dialogue that help create this feeling.

Difficulty: *Easy*

Objective: *Essay*

Selection Test B, p. 31

Critical Reading

1. ANS: B	DIF: Average	OBJ: Literary Analysis
2. ANS: C	DIF: Average	OBJ: Interpretation
3. ANS: A	DIF: Challenging	OBJ: Interpretation
4. ANS: D	DIF: Challenging	OBJ: Reading Skill
5. ANS: C	DIF: Challenging	OBJ: Comprehension
6. ANS: A	DIF: Average	OBJ: Literary Analysis
7. ANS: B	DIF: Average	OBJ: Interpretation
8. ANS: C	DIF: Challenging	OBJ: Literary Analysis
9. ANS: A	DIF: Average	OBJ: Literary Analysis
10. ANS: B	DIF: Average	OBJ: Comprehension
11. ANS: C	DIF: Challenging	OBJ: Interpretation
12. ANS: D	DIF: Challenging	OBJ: Reading Skill
13. ANS: A	DIF: Average	OBJ: Reading Skill
14. ANS: A	DIF: Average	OBJ: Interpretation
15. ANS: C	DIF: Average	OBJ: Comprehension

Vocabulary and Grammar

16. ANS: B	DIF: Average	OBJ: Vocabulary
17. ANS: D	DIF: Average	OBJ: Vocabulary
18. ANS: B	DIF: Challenging	OBJ: Vocabulary
19. ANS: B	DIF: Average	OBJ: Grammar

Essay

20. Students' essays should discuss the theme conveyed by one of the four poems. For example, "The Guitar" conveys the insight that the sound of music can powerfully reflect our deepest losses and longings; "The Bridegroom" conveys that standing up to evil can be a frightening, but ultimately rewarding, experience; "The Fish" conveys that compassion can be a powerful motivation and that people can relate to the struggles of other creatures; "Danny Deever" conveys the message that soldiers form deep bonds and are deeply affected by the deaths of their comrades. Students should describe how the poem's imagery, dialogue, or action help convey the theme.

Difficulty: *Average*

Objective: *Essay*

21. Students' essays should identify one lyric poem (either "The Guitar" or "The Fish") and one narrative poem (either "The Bridegroom" or "Danny Deever"). They should then summarize the main impression conveyed by the lyric poem and the story told in the narrative poem. Students who prefer the lyric poem may cite its vivid imagery or its strong emotional quality as reasons. Students who prefer the narrative poem may cite the appeal of its characters, dialogue, plot, and suspense in holding their interest.

Difficulty: *Average*

Objective: *Essay*

22. Students' essays should reflect the following points: In "The Fish," the speaker catches an old fish that has escaped others' hooks five times before, and she decides to let it go. She is proud of having finally caught the fish, but she feels admiration and compassion for its previous heroic struggles. Her decision conveys the power and rewards of compassion. In "The Bridegroom," Natasha experiences conflict over an arranged marriage with a man she knows as a murderer. She does not want to explain how she knows about the murder, but she is terrified of marrying such an evil man. She invites the police to the wedding and decides to tell the story of the murder as if it were a dream. The Bridegroom reveals his guilt and is arrested. The poem conveys the message that a person of courage and intelligence can sometimes find a way to stand up to evil. Students should also explain techniques each poet uses to create suspense until the final decision is made.

Difficulty: *Challenging*

Objective: *Essay*

Poetry Collection: Denise Levertov, William Carlos Williams, Robert Frost, and Naomi Shihab Nye

Vocabulary Warm-up Exercises, p. 35

A. 1. unanswerable
   2. sluggish
   3. moisten
   4. burden
   5. dignity
   6. confidence

B. Sample Answers

1. Yes, most essay writers should try to achieve *clarity* because they want to explain their ideas clearly.
2. The *outermost* areas of Hawaii include beaches and coastline, while the central regions often include volcanoes.
3. Yes, germs that cause the common cold can be *contagious* as they spread from person to person.
4. Yes; music might calm someone down and help him or her relax enough to find effective strategies for reducing *woes*, or troubles.
5. An electrical *surge* in a computer lab could cause damage to data stored electronically in computer memory.

Reading Warm-up A, p. 36

Sample Answers

1. (Spring rains); I would *moisten* a dry mouth by drinking water.
2. arrives late; Someone who is *sluggish* feels slow and heavy.
3. everyone has a unique response to spring; I think that the question "Is there life after death" is *unanswerable* because we will never know for sure during our lifetime.
4. Expecting one poem to explain everything about spring; A student carrying fifteen textbooks to school has a heavy *burden*.
5. (nobility) (goodness); *Dignity* is a sense of honor and being worthy of the respect of others.
6. certain that his impression of spring is accurate; I feel *confidence* about the American history test that I will take next week.

Reading Warm-up B, p. 37

Sample Answers

1. They stopped by for lunch and ended up staying for days; Many diseases, such as the common cold, are *contagious*.
2. Stores never opened; There was no food to eat; *Woes* are troubles or misfortunes.
3. (central); *Outermost* means "at the outer edges of something."
4. let people know that they could trust everything she said and did; Mr. Waterson is *earnest* because everything he says is serious and true.
5. something important seemed obvious for the first time; *Clarity* means "the quality of being clear or easily understandable."
6. (a surge of activity); If our school experienced a *surge* of creativity, everyone might start writing poems or painting pictures.

Poetry Collection: Denise Levertov, William Carlos Williams, Robert Frost, and Naomi Shihab Nye

Literary Analysis: Narrative and Lyric Poetry, p. 38

1. A. The speaker is a tree.
   B. The tree tells about how it and other trees around it responded to hearing Orpheus sing and play the lyre. The trees were so moved by the music that, when Orpheus left, they uprooted themselves and followed him, so that they could continue hearing his music.
2. The imagery suggests that the new life of spring occurs gradually. It seems struggling and uncertain at first because it is so unprotected, and the world is so cold.
3. *Answers may include feeble-pointed spikes*—appeals to touch and sight; *pale*—appeals to sight; *bright green*—sight; *whispered*—hearing.
4. A. The speaker of "Making a Fist" is a woman telling a true story about an incident from her childhood.
   B. On a car trip when she was seven, the speaker was suddenly afraid that she was dying. She asked her mother how people could tell if they were dying. Her mother said that dying people could no longer make a fist. The woman says that years later she still finds herself clenching and unclenching her hand to prove to herself that she is alive.

Reading: Read Aloud and Adjust Reading Rate to Read Fluently, p. 39

1. A. The lines make one complete sentence.
   B. Readers should pause briefly after the words *then* and *length*.
2. A. Students should underline the adjectives *naked*, *cold, uncertain, cold,* and *familiar.*
   B. Students should bracket as follows: [They enter the new world naked,] [cold,] [uncertain of all save that they enter.] [All about them] [the cold, familiar wind.]
3. A. The lines include a question mark, a semicolon, a comma, a dash, and a period.
   B. Question mark—Read in a questioning tone and then pause. Semicolon—Read as the answer to a question and then pause. Comma—Pause briefly. Dash—Pause and then read the following statement as an explanation. Period—Long pause.
4. Line 7 should be read in the tone of voice of a child begging her mother for important information. Line 11 should be read in the voice of a confident adult, reassuring a child.

Vocabulary Builder, p. 40

A. 1. Students should describe a situation in which a person would be scared or angry.
2. Students could describe a winter scene in which trees are bare.
3. Students should describe reading, watching TV, or playing games.
4. Students should describe a situation that would cause a person great distress.

B. 1. B; 2. A; 3. D; 4. B

Enrichment: Greek Mythology, p. 43

1. Levertov focuses on the detail of how Orpheus was able to inspire the trees to follow him through the power of his song. She also describes the details of how he was killed.
2. The myth reveals that the Greeks felt that music and love were sources of great power in human life. The power of Orpheus's love song is able to uproot trees and even bring a dead woman back to life.
3. Orpheus lives on through the beauty of the nightingales' song above his grave and through the eternal presence of his lyre in the night sky as a constellation. These details suggest that no one can ever really destroy the power of music.

Poetry Collections: Alexander Pushkin, Federico García Lorca, Elizabeth Bishop, Rudyard Kipling; Denise Levertov, William Carlos Williams, Robert Frost, and Naomi Shihab Nye

Build Language Skills: Vocabulary, p. 44

A. 1. annoyance
2. performance
3. avoidance
4. resemblance

B. 1. Students should describe an extreme or dramatic change they would like to see in their communities.
2. People with differing opinions should communicate so that they can better understand each other's points of view.
3. Sample response: The apples are piled high inside the browned, hardened crust.
4. Students should identify an event and explain why it was important.
5. I could make up for damaging someone's property by apologizing and by paying for the damage.

Build Language Skills: Grammar, p. 45

A. 1. phrase: for Alex; preposition: for; object: Alex
2. phrase: of the United States; preposition: of; object: United States; phrase: during the Civil War; preposition: during; object: Civil War

3. phrase: around the moon; preposition: around; object: moon
4. phrase: Among my favorite possessions; preposition: among; object: possessions; phrase: from my grandmother; preposition: from; object: grandmother
5. phrase: to the dance; preposition: to; object: dance; phrase: after the game; preposition: after; object: game
6. phrase: on the left; preposition: on; object: left
7. phrase: of the game; preposition: of; object: game; phrase: to the riddle; preposition: to; object: riddle
8. phrase: toward the wall; preposition: toward; object: wall
9. phrase: between Mars and Venus; preposition: between; objects: Mars, Venus
10. phrase: with the ball; preposition: with; object: ball; phrase: in your hands; preposition: in; object: hands; phrase: against the rules; preposition: against; object: rules; phrase: of the game; preposition: of; object: game

B. Students' paragraphs should describe a room, using spatial order. They should include prepositional phrases that describe the position of objects in relation to one another.

Poetry Collection: Denise Levertov, William Carlos Williams, Robert Frost, and Naomi Shihab Nye

Selection Test A, p. 46

Critical Reading

1. ANS: B	DIF: Easy	OBJ: Literary Analysis
2. ANS: C	DIF: Easy	OBJ: Comprehension
3. ANS: A	DIF: Easy	OBJ: Interpretation
4. ANS: C	DIF: Easy	OBJ: Literary Analysis
5. ANS: D	DIF: Easy	OBJ: Reading
6. ANS: B	DIF: Easy	OBJ: Interpretation
7. ANS: C	DIF: Easy	OBJ: Comprehension
8. ANS: A	DIF: Easy	OBJ: Literary Analysis
9. ANS: B	DIF: Easy	OBJ: Reading
10. ANS: A	DIF: Easy	OBJ: Comprehension
11. ANS: A	DIF: Easy	OBJ: Interpretation
12. ANS: D	DIF: Easy	OBJ: Interpretation

Vocabulary and Grammar

13. ANS: B	DIF: Easy	OBJ: Vocabulary
14. ANS: A	DIF: Easy	OBJ: Vocabulary
15. ANS: C	DIF: Easy	OBJ: Grammar

Essay

16. Students may summarize the story told in "A Tree Telling of Orpheus" or "Making a Fist." "Orpheus" is set in ancient Greece. Characters include the tree who is speaking, the other trees around it, and Orpheus. The tree tells how it was so moved by Orpheus's music that it and the other trees uprooted themselves and followed Orpheus. Orpheus taught the trees to dance, then sang their roots back into the earth. As the trees hope for his return, they feel that Orpheus has changed them forever. "Making a Fist" is set during a car trip when the speaker was seven and also in the present. The main characters are the speaker (now a grown woman) and her mother. The speaker describes how she felt that she was dying during the car trip. She begged her mother to explain how people could tell if they were dying. Her mother said you were dying if you could no longer make a fist. As a grown woman, the speaker smiles at the wisdom of this advice and admits that she still feels like a child making a fist in the backseat of a car.
    Difficulty: *Easy*
    Objective: *Essay*

17. Students should accurately describe the emotional impact of one of the four poems. They should cite descriptions, events, or dialogue that help create this feeling.
    Difficulty: *Easy*
    Objective: *Essay*

Selection Test B, p. 49

Critical Reading

1. ANS: B	DIF: Average	OBJ: Literary Analysis
2. ANS: C	DIF: Average	OBJ: Interpretation
3. ANS: C	DIF: Challenging	OBJ: Interpretation
4. ANS: B	DIF: Challenging	OBJ: Reading
5. ANS: D	DIF: Average	OBJ: Comprehension
6. ANS: A	DIF: Average	OBJ: Literary Analysis
7. ANS: B	DIF: Challenging	OBJ: Interpretation
8. ANS: A	DIF: Average	OBJ: Literary Analysis
9. ANS: A	DIF: Average	OBJ: Literary Analysis
10. ANS: B	DIF: Average	OBJ: Comprehension
11. ANS: C	DIF: Challenging	OBJ: Interpretation
12. ANS: D	DIF: Challenging	OBJ: Reading
13. ANS: B	DIF: Average	OBJ: Literary Analysis
14. ANS: C	DIF: Average	OBJ: Interpretation
15. ANS: D	DIF: Challenging	OBJ: Interpretation
16. ANS: C	DIF: Average	OBJ: Reading

Vocabulary and Grammar

17. ANS: B	DIF: Average	OBJ: Vocabulary
18. ANS: D	DIF: Average	OBJ: Vocabulary
19. ANS: B	DIF: Average	OBJ: Grammar
20. ANS: A	DIF: Challenging	OBJ: Grammar

Essay

21. Students' essays should discuss the theme, or message, conveyed by one of the four poems. For example, "A Tree Telling of Orpheus" conveys the insight that hearing music is a powerful emotional experience; "Spring and All" conveys that the birth of new life is a dangerous process involving struggle and uncertainty; "Mowing" conveys that hard physical work can be a labor of love; "Making a Fist" conveys that life is a difficult journey and that coming to terms with death is a lifelong process. Students should describe how the poem's imagery, dialogue, or action help convey the theme.
    Difficulty: *Average*
    Objective: *Essay*

22. Students' essays should identify one lyric poem (either "Spring and All" or "Mowing") and one narrative poem (either "A Tree Telling of Orpheus" or "Making a Fist"). They should then summarize the main impression conveyed by the lyric poem and the story told in the narrative poem. Students who prefer the lyric poem may cite its vivid imagery or its strong emotional quality as reasons for its appeal. Students who prefer the narrative poem may cite the appeal of its characters, dialogue, plot, and suspense in holding their interest.
    Difficulty: *Average*
    Objective: *Essay*

23. Students' essays should evaluate the effectiveness of using a tree as the speaker of the poem. They should answer each question and include details that support their answers. Students should also mention parts of the narrative in which the technique of using a nonhuman speaker does or does not work well.
    Difficulty: *Challenging*
    Objective: *Essay*

Poetry Collection: Ki Tsurayuki, Minamoto no Toshiyori, James Weldon Johnson, and Dylan Thomas

Vocabulary Warm-up Exercises, p. 53

A. 1. patient
2. throbbing
3. fierce
4. avenues
5. brighter
6. gentle

B. Sample Answers

1. *Clustering* weeds would be gathered together, not scattered and isolated.
2. If my friend *grieved* after hearing some news, I would expect her to be sad.
3. If people live in *stark* conditions, they do not have many material comforts.
4. If someone's wit is *subtle*, probably not everyone could appreciate it.

5. If I am on the *threshold* of a career, I am not already working in it.

6. If I felt *unutterable* sadness, it would be too intense or painful for me to put into words.

Reading Warm-up A, p. 54

Sample Answers

1. (light); *Brighter* means "shining with more light."

2. (Thomas's); *Throbbing* means "beating strongly and steadily."

3. waited many years for; You need to be *patient* if you are waiting for someone to finish composing a symphony.

4. (fierce); I felt a *gentle* breeze at twilight.

5. Dylan Thomas is the "fierce genius." The music reflects the poetry of this sometimes gentle, sometimes *wild* genius.

6. (Ninth and Tenth *Avenues*); I like Park and West End *Avenues*. Both are wide, residential streets with lots of sunlight and beautiful old buildings.

Reading Warm-up B, p. 55

Sample Answers

1. the world of fame and success; *Threshold* means "a point of beginning."

2. African Americans might have begun *clustering* in Harlem because it was easier to live in a community filled with other African Americans. *Gathering* is a synonym for *clustering*.

3. (obvious); I was the only one who appreciated his *subtle* charms.

4. The history of African Americans before 1900 could be described as *stark* because up until a few years before that, they had worked as slaves. Life in solitary confinement would be very *stark*.

5. (injustice), (racism); If injustice and racism are *unutterable*, they also are horrible and heartbreaking.

6. (died), (tragic); I *grieved* for my cat when it was missing.

Poetry Collection: Ki Tsurayuki, Minamoto no Toshiyori, James Weldon Johnson, and Dylan Thomas

Literary Analysis: Poetic Form, p. 56

1. The translation of "The clustering clouds. . ." is a better example of tanka form because the words in each line have the correct number of syllables for the form: 5, 7, 5, 7, 7.

2. A. When I come down to sleep death's endless night,
   The threshold of the unknown dark to cross,
   What to me then will be the keenest loss,
   When this bright world blurs on my fading sight?

   B. Each line has five unaccented and five accented syllables.

   C. The rhyme scheme is abba.

   D. "The City" is written in sonnet form.

3. A. There are three lines in each stanza.
   B. The rhyme scheme is aba, aba.
   C. Line 1 is repeated.
   D. "Do Not Go Gentle" is written in villanelle form.

Reading: Preview a Poem to Read Fluently, p. 57

1. The punctuation marks are a comma and a period.

2. The dash indicates a pause and that what follows will be a reflection about clouds. The question mark indicates that the speaker wonders about the clouds. The period indicates that the last two lines explain the point the speaker wants to make about the clouds and the moonlight.

3. A. There are three end marks in lines 1–8.
   B. The first two are question marks. The third is a period.
   C. Lines 1–7 should be read as two questions. Line 8 should be read as the answer to the questions.
   D. An exclamation point is used twice in lines 9–14.
   E. The last six lines should be read with great feeling.

4. A. Each stanza contains one complete sentence.
   B. Each stanza should be read as one complete thought, or point, that the speaker wants to make about death.
   C. The word *rage* is repeated.
   D. The poem should be read with a feeling of anger, or passionate resistance, against the necessity of death.

Vocabulary Builder, p. 58

A. 1. true: In the fall, many birds gather in groups to migrate for the winter.

2. false: A lunar eclipse is an eclipse of the moon.

3. false: Chimneys are located on the roofs of buildings, not in the doorways.

4. true: A frail person is weak and has bones that are easily broken. Such a person is likely to suffer serious injuries from falling on the ice.

B. 1. C; 2. A; 3. D

Enrichment: Poetry in Ancient Japanese Culture, p. 61

1. In "When I went to visit. . .," the birds on the river are suffering in the cold, like the speaker of the poem, who has come out on a winter night to visit his love. The speaker of "The clustering clouds" thinks about the contrasts that clouds offer as they cluster and then clear on a moonlit night.

2. Instead of giving details about the girl and why he loves her so much, the speaker simply describes his impressions of nature on the cold winter night he went to visit her. The fact that he would go out on such a bitter night suggests the power of his love.

3. Some students may prefer literature that explores feelings more explicitly and in more detail, because it gives them a deeper understanding of a speaker's or character's perspective. Others may feel that the tanka's use of imagery to capture a moment in time leaves a more lasting emotional impression on the reader.

Selection Test A, p. 62

Critical Reading

1. ANS: C	DIF: Easy	OBJ: Literary Analysis
2. ANS: B	DIF: Easy	OBJ: Comprehension
3. ANS: A	DIF: Easy	OBJ: Interpretation
4. ANS: B	DIF: Easy	OBJ: Comprehension
5. ANS: C	DIF: Easy	OBJ: Reading Strategy
6. ANS: A	DIF: Easy	OBJ: Literary Analysis
7. ANS: B	DIF: Easy	OBJ: Comprehension
8. ANS: B	DIF: Easy	OBJ: Reading Strategy
9. ANS: C	DIF: Easy	OBJ: Literary Analysis
10. ANS: B	DIF: Easy	OBJ: Interpretation
11. ANS: A	DIF: Easy	OBJ: Literary Analysis
12. ANS: C	DIF: Easy	OBJ: Comprehension

Vocabulary and Grammar

13. ANS: B	DIF: Easy	OBJ: Vocabulary
14. ANS: C	DIF: Easy	OBJ: Vocabulary
15. ANS: B	DIF: Easy	OBJ: Grammar

Essay

16. Students who choose "When I went to visit. . ." might discuss the poem's brevity and the image of crying birds on a cold winter night, as well as the subject matter of love. Students who choose "The clustering clouds. . ." might discuss its brevity and the vivid image of moonlight breaking through the clearing clouds. Students who choose "My City" might discuss its regular pattern of rhythm and rhyme, its quatrains that make different points, its emotional closing couplet, and its imagery celebrating urban life. Students who choose "Do Not Go Gentle Into That Good Night" might cite its pattern of rhythm and rhyme, its short stanzas, the repetition of key lines, its vivid imagery, its emotional subject matter, and its passionate tone.

Difficulty: *Easy*

Objective: *Essay*

17. Students who choose "My City" should say that it tries to convince the reader that the greatest loss death will bring the speaker is his inability to experience and participate in the excitement of city life: its sights, sounds, and smells. Students who choose "Do Not Go Gentle Into That Good Night" should say that the speaker tries to convince readers that old people should not calmly accept death but should "rage" against it, holding on

fiercely to each moment of life that remains. In several stanzas, the speaker gives reasons why different types of men all have cause to regret that they did not make the most of their lives, so they should all fight against the finality of death.

Difficulty: *Easy*

Objective: *Essay*

Selection Test B, p. 65

Critical Reading

1. ANS: A	DIF: Average	OBJ: Literary Analysis
2. ANS: D	DIF: Challenging	OBJ: Literary Analysis
3. ANS: D	DIF: Challenging	OBJ: Reading Skill
4. ANS: B	DIF: Average	OBJ: Interpretation
5. ANS: C	DIF: Average	OBJ: Interpretation
6. ANS: A	DIF: Average	OBJ: Literary Analysis
7. ANS: C	DIF: Challenging	OBJ: Literary Analysis
8. ANS: D	DIF: Average	OBJ: Interpretation
9. ANS: B	DIF: Average	OBJ: Reading Strategy
10. ANS: C	DIF: Average	OBJ: Interpretation
11. ANS: C	DIF: Average	OBJ: Comprehension
12. ANS: C	DIF: Average	OBJ: Literary Analysis
13. ANS: A	DIF: Challenging	OBJ: Reading Skill
14. ANS: C	DIF: Challenging	OBJ: Interpretation
15. ANS: B	DIF: Challenging	OBJ: Literary Analysis

Vocabulary and Grammar

16. ANS: D	DIF: Challenging	OBJ: Vocabulary
17. ANS: B	DIF: Average	OBJ: Vocabulary
18. ANS: A	DIF: Average	OBJ: Vocabulary
19. ANS: D	DIF: Challenging	OBJ: Grammar

Essay

20. Both poems describe the losses and regrets that dying brings. "My City" tries to convince the reader that the greatest loss death will bring is not the speaker's inability to enjoy nature, but his inability to experience and participate in the excitement of city life: its sights, sounds, and smells. "Do Not Go Gentle Into That Good Night" tries to convince readers that old people should not calmly accept death but should "rage" against it, holding on fiercely to each moment of life that remains. In several stanzas, the speaker gives reasons why different types of men have cause for regret. Therefore, all should fight against the finality of death.

Difficulty: *Average*

Objective: *Essay*

21. Students who choose one of the tanka should explain how the poem's brevity and imagery create the effect of a mysterious "snapshot," capturing one moment in time

and suggesting the speaker's intense feelings about that moment. Students who choose "My City" or "Do Not Go Gentle Into That Good Night" should describe the cumulative emotional impact of rhythm and rhyme, repetition, and detailed imagery that elaborates on an argument or supports a state of mind.

Difficulty: *Average*
Objective: *Essay*

22. Students' essays should accurately summarize Thomas's point of view about resisting death and should give two or three specific reasons why they agree or disagree with it. Students should give details from the poem to support their reasoning.

Difficulty: *Challenging*
Objective: *Essay*

Poetry Collection: Priest Jakuren, Ono Komachi, Theodore Roethke, and William Shakespeare

Vocabulary Warm-up Exercises, p. 69

A. 1. nature
2. waking
3. winding
4. lowly
5. compare
6. being

B. Sample Answers

1. When I am experiencing anger or jealousy, I do not have a *temperate* response.
2. My *complexion* shows some wrinkles when I frown.
3. I do not have any important belongings currently in my *possession*.
4. I feel that some values, such as compassion and love, are *eternal*.
5. Occasionally, I have felt some *loneliness* when I am by myself.

Reading Warm-up A, p. 70

Sample Answers

1. (early that mid-October morning); *Sleeping* and *slumbering* are antonyms for *waking*.
2. up the mountain outside of town; *Nature* is "everything that exists in the world that is not made by humans, such as animals, plants, weather, and so on."
3. (trail); *Winding* means "curving or bending."
4. because this was the first time they had tried to cover so much ground; *Compare* means "to examine or judge two or more things in order to show how they are similar to or different from each other."
5. from the top of his head to the soles of his feet; The fear of the darkened hallway filled my whole *being*, and every muscle tensed.
6. (ant); *Lowly* means "low in rank or importance."

Reading Warm-up B, p. 71

Sample Answers

1. love, death, and immortality; Literary themes such as experiencing romantic love, growing up, and struggles for power are *eternal*.
2. "*Die single and thine image dies with thee.*" A *sonnet* is "a fourteen-line poem, usually rhyming."
3. *Solitude* is a synonym for *loneliness*; I experienced *loneliness* when my brothers and sisters went on a trip and I stayed home.
4. (black); My *complexion* is pale and dry.
5. (mild); Her reaction to the tragedy was surprisingly *temperate*.
6. adequate information to determine just who Shakespeare's Fair Youth and Dark Lady were; Scholars might not be in *possession* of this information because Shakespeare wrote about people and events from so long ago.

Poetry Collection: Priest Jakuren, Ono Komachi, Theodore Roethke, and William Shakespeare

Literary Analysis: Poetic Form, p. 72

1. A. The translation of "One cannot ask loneliness. . ." is only four lines long, instead of the traditional five. Its syllable counts are 7, 5, 6, 4, instead of the traditional 5, 7, 5, 7, 7. The translation of "Was it that I went to sleep" follows tanka form in being five lines long, but its syllable count is 7, 4, 6, 6, 6.
   B. *Sample answer:* The translator believed that conveying the imagery and feeling of the Japanese poem was more important than exactly matching the syllable and line counts.
2. A. There are three lines in each stanza.
   B. The rhyme scheme is aba, aba.
   C. Line 1 is repeated.
   D. "The Waking" is written in villanelle form.
3. A. Shall I compare thee to a summer's day?
   Thou art more lovely and more temperate:
   Rough winds do shake the darling buds of May,
   And summer's lease hath all too short a date:
   B. Each line has five unaccented and five accented syllables.
   C. The rhyme scheme is abab.

Reading: Preview a Poem to Read Fluently, p. 73

1. There are two periods in the poem.
2. The first three lines should be read as one question. The last two lines should be read as a reflection on, or a response to, the question.

3. A. There are seven end marks in lines 1–6.
   B. Readers should pause after each line and also in the middle of line 4.
   C. Because there are so many pauses, the lines must be read slowly, which reflects the meaning of "take my waking slow." The meaning and theme of the poem are revealed gradually, line by line, which reflects the wisdom of "I learn by going where I have to go."

4. The words *temperate* and *eternal* are key to understanding the poem's meaning and mood. The speaker loves the beloved because she is more *temperate* than summer, meaning she is not subject to extreme changes, the way the seasons are. He also wants to assure her that her beauty is *eternal*, because she will live on in his poem forever.

Vocabulary Builder, p. 74

A. 1. false: A child's destiny—what will happen to him or her in life—cannot be predicted in advance.

2. false: Winters in northern latitudes often bring extremely low temperatures rather than mild weather.

3. true: People often use a good education to help them earn a career that has high status or pay.

4. false: An eternal mystery is one that is everlasting; it can never be solved.

B. 1. C; 2. D; 3. A

Enrichment: Waking, Sleeping, Dreaming, p. 77

1. Students' responses will depend on whether they tend to be logical/analytic thinkers or visual and linguistic learners. Answers should cite details from the essay or from the poems "Was it that I went to sleep. . ." and "The Waking."

2. Recent evidence suggests that people have some of their most creative ideas when they are just waking up, in an in-between state of consciousness. A poet might want to use this time as a source of ideas. Some lines from "The Waking" might suggest characteristics of a "flow state." For example, "What falls away is always. And is near."; "We think by feeling. What is there to know?"; "I hear my being dance from ear to ear."; and "Light takes the Tree; but who can tell us how?"

Poetry Collections: Ki Tsurayuki, Minamoto no Toshiyori, James Weldon Johnson, Dylan Thomas; Priest Jakuren, Ono Komachi, Theodore Roethke, and William Shakespeare

Build Language Skills: Vocabulary, p. 78

A. 1. marginal
2. traditional
3. organizational
4. logical

B. 1. Students might give hip-hop, classical, or country music as examples of how *diverse* modern music is.

2. Students might describe a car that does not pollute the air or that protects passengers from serious injuries as a *radical* improvement.

3. Students should explain why the Internet is important to them for research, communicating with friends, or entertainment.

4. People *compensate* for poor vision by wearing glasses or contact lenses. People *compensate* for poor hearing by wearing hearing aids.

5. Students might say that the blackness of the night sky and its shining stars make them feel small or awed.

Build Language Skills: Grammar, p. 79

A. 1. direct object is *movies*
2. direct object is *DVDs*
3. no d.o.
4. no d.o.
5. direct object is *me*

B. Students should write a paragraph about an activity they enjoy and underline all direct objects in the paragraph.

Poetry Collection: Priest Jakuren, Ono Komachi, Theodore Roethke, and William Shakespeare

Selection Test A, p. 80

Critical Reading

1. ANS: C	DIF: Easy		OBJ: Literary Analysis
2. ANS: C	DIF: Easy		OBJ: Reading
3. ANS: A	DIF: Easy		OBJ: Comprehension
4. ANS: C	DIF: Easy		OBJ: Comprehension
5. ANS: B	DIF: Easy		OBJ: Interpretation
6. ANS: C	DIF: Easy		OBJ: Literary Analysis
7. ANS: A	DIF: Easy		OBJ: Literary Analysis
8. ANS: D	DIF: Easy		OBJ: Interpretation
9. ANS: A	DIF: Easy		OBJ: Literary Analysis
10. ANS: B	DIF: Easy		OBJ: Comprehension
11. ANS: B	DIF: Easy		OBJ: Reading
12. ANS: D	DIF: Easy		OBJ: Interpretation

Vocabulary and Grammar

13. ANS: D	DIF: Easy		OBJ: Vocabulary
14. ANS: C	DIF: Easy		OBJ: Vocabulary
15. ANS: B	DIF: Easy		OBJ: Grammar

Essay

16. Students who choose "One cannot ask loneliness. . ." might discuss the poem's brevity and the image of evergreen trees on a mountain in fall, as well as the subject matter of loneliness. Students who choose "Was it that I went to sleep. . ." might discuss the poem's brevity and the subject matter of dreams. Students who choose "The Waking" might cite its pattern of rhythm and rhyme, its short sentences and stanzas, the repetition of key lines, its vivid imagery, and the sense of mytery it creates about waking, sleeping, and being alive. Students who choose Sonnet 18 might discuss its regular pattern of rhythm and rhyme, its quatrains that each make a different point, its emotional closing couplet, and its subject matter of romantic love.

    Difficulty: *Easy*

    Objective: *Essay*

17. Students who choose "Was it that I went to sleep. . ." might mention the speaker's puzzlement about what caused her to dream of the man she loves. They may also discuss her disappointment at discovering that the dream was not real. Students who choose "The Waking" might cite the line "I take my waking slow" as a vivid description of how waking up to the "real world" can be a gradual process and how going through our daily lives often feels like a dream.

    Difficulty: *Easy*

    Objective: *Essay*

Selection Test B, p. 83

Critical Reading

1. ANS: A	DIF: Average	OBJ: Literary Analysis
2. ANS: D	DIF: Challenging	OBJ: Literary Analysis
3. ANS: B	DIF: Average	OBJ: Comprehension
4. ANS: B	DIF: Average	OBJ: Reading
5. ANS: C	DIF: Average	OBJ: Interpretation
6. ANS: B	DIF: Average	OBJ: Comprehension
7. ANS: A	DIF: Challenging	OBJ: Interpretation
8. ANS: C	DIF: Average	OBJ: Literary Analysis
9. ANS: B	DIF: Challenging	OBJ: Reading
10. ANS: C	DIF: Average	OBJ: Literary Analysis
11. ANS: A	DIF: Average	OBJ: Literary Analysis
12. ANS: C	DIF: Challenging	OBJ: Literary Analysis
13. ANS: C	DIF: Average	OBJ: Reading
14. ANS: C	DIF: Challenging	OBJ: Comprehension
15. ANS: B	DIF: Challenging	OBJ: Literary Analysis

Vocabulary and Grammar

16. ANS: D	DIF: Average	OBJ: Vocabulary
17. ANS: B	DIF: Challenging	OBJ: Vocabulary
18. ANS: A	DIF: Average	OBJ: Vocabulary
19. ANS: D	DIF: Challenging	OBJ: Grammar

Essay

20. Students who choose one of the tanka should explain how the poem's brevity and imagery create the effect of a mysterious "snapshot," capturing one moment in time and suggesting the speaker's intense feelings about that moment. Students who choose Sonnet 18 or "The Waking" should describe the cumulative emotional impact of rhythm and rhyme, repetition, and detailed imagery that elaborates on an argument or supports a state of mind.

    Difficulty: *Average*

    Objective: *Essay*

21. Students who choose line 1 should explain that it promotes a slow, thoughtful approach to life. Students who choose line 2 should explain that it promotes searching for one's destiny by noticing the kinds of situations that draw us into taking risks, despite our fears of failure. Students who choose line 3 should explain its view that we learn who we truly are only by experience, by going forward in events and situations that seem important to us. In their essays, students should evaluate the wisdom of the line they chose and give at least two examples of situations in life in which such an approach is wise or unwise.

    Difficulty: *Average*

    Objective: *Essay*

22. Students' essays should include the following points: In Sonnet 18, the speaker argues that his beloved's beauty is perfect and will last forever, because he is immortalizing her. In the first quatrain, he compares her to a summer's day and says she is superior to a summer's day because she is "more lovely and more temperate." In the second quatrain, he gives examples of how even the most perfect day has imperfect moments and does not last. In the third quatrain, he claims that his beloved's beauty, in contrast, will last forever. Death cannot diminish it. In the couplet, he explains why her beauty will last forever. He is immortalizing it in this poem: As long as people can read, her beauty will live on.

    Difficulty: *Challenging*

    Objective: *Essay*

Poetry by Gabriela Mistral, Gwendolyn Brooks, and John Keats

Vocabulary Warm-up Exercises, p. 87

A. 1. meadow
   2. casual
   3. receipts
   4. haggard
   5. horrid
   6. withered

B. Sample Answers

1. The young men *loitering* in the park stood near the pond for hours.
2. We always *sojourn* at the lake cabin, so we will spend a few days there as usual.
3. The group was only for highly skilled members of the military, so membership was limited to *warriors*.
4. The teenager was *woebegone* when the boy she liked did not ask her to the party.
5. Danny was in *thrall* to his coach, so he always listened to him.

Reading Warm-up A, p. 88

Sample Answers

1. flowers; A *meadow* is "a field with wild grass and flowers."
2. (in the winter); *Withered* means "shriveled; dried up."
3. (comfortable); Her relaxed, *casual* dinner made us all feel at home.
4. Grandma said that he was sick; My father looked *haggard* when he had a cold.
5. (medical); *Receipts* are "pieces of paper showing that you have received money or goods."
6. that Grandpa would not undergo treatments because of money; *Horrid* means "extremely bad or difficult."

Reading Warm-up B, p. 89

Sample Answers

1. when deserted by the woman he loves; *Anguish* is "suffering caused by extreme pain or worry."
2. I saw several older men *loitering* in the park one day.
3. A knight silently in *thrall* to a lady might try to get her attention through his looks and actions.
4. battle in their lady's name; The medieval *warriors* were not afraid of battle.
5. The knights might *travel* to a place far from home to try to bring back a famous object.
6. *Forlorn* is a synonym for *woebegone*. I felt *woebegone* and alone when my parents left town for a week.

Poetry by Gabriela Mistral, Gwendolyn Brooks, and John Keats

Literary Analysis: Tone and Mood, p. 90

1. A. a mother's fear of losing her daughter
   B. the image of a swallow flying away; the image of a little girl playing in the meadow; the image of a distant queen
   C. a mother's deep love for her child
2. A. remembering
   B. happy and sad memories
   C. respectful, because the couple is described as "Mostly Good"

3. A. in the countryside by a lake in late autumn
   B. include alone, palely loitering, haggard, woebegone
   C. include dreamy, romantic, heartbroken, mysterious, and so on

Vocabulary Builder, p. 91

A. 1. sojourn
2. thrall
3. haggard

B. Sample Answers

1. I feel tired and <u>worn out</u> after studying all night.
2. When she is in the <u>grip</u> of a mystery novel, it is impossible to get her attention.
3. We enjoyed a two-week <u>stay</u> at my uncle's mountain cabin.

C. 1. B; 2. D

Selection Test A, p. 93

Critical Reading

1. ANS: D	DIF: Easy	OBJ: Comprehension
2. ANS: A	DIF: Easy	OBJ: Interpretation
3. ANS: D	DIF: Easy	OBJ: Literary Analysis
4. ANS: B	DIF: Easy	OBJ: Interpretation
5. ANS: A	DIF: Easy	OBJ: Literary Analysis
6. ANS: C	DIF: Easy	OBJ: Comprehension
7. ANS: B	DIF: Easy	OBJ: Comprehension
8. ANS: D	DIF: Easy	OBJ: Interpretation
9. ANS: A	DIF: Easy	OBJ: Comprehension
10. ANS: D	DIF: Easy	OBJ: Literary Analysis
11. ANS: C	DIF: Easy	OBJ: Interpretation
12. ANS: B	DIF: Easy	OBJ: Literary Analysis
13. ANS: C	DIF: Easy	OBJ: Literary Analysis

Vocabulary

14. ANS: D	DIF: Easy	OBJ: Vocabulary
15. ANS: B	DIF: Easy	OBJ: Vocabulary

Essay

16. Students may respond that "The Bean Eaters" or "Fear" paints the most positive view of love because each poem shows a strong family bond between two people. Students may respond that "La Belle Dame sans Merci" or "Fear" paints the most negative picture of love because each describes or expresses the pain that goes with the loss of a loved one. Accept all other reasonable responses.

Difficulty: *Easy*

Objective: *Essay*

17. Students will likely state that the authors express affection and/or pity for the characters in all three poems. They may respond that Mistral chose to write about the mother in "Fear" because her feelings of fear and love are experienced by most mothers, that Brooks chose to write about the "bean eaters" because the old couple reminds us of what is truly important in life, and that Keats chose to write about the knight to warn readers against foolish, romantic love.

Difficulty: *Easy*
Objective: *Essay*

Selection Test B, p. 96

Critical Reading

1. ANS: C	DIF: Average	OBJ: Literary Analysis
2. ANS: C	DIF: Average	OBJ: Interpretation
3. ANS: D	DIF: Average	OBJ: Comprehension
4. ANS: A	DIF: Average	OBJ: Interpretation
5. ANS: B	DIF: Average	OBJ: Comprehension
6. ANS: D	DIF: Average	OBJ: Literary Analysis
7. ANS: A	DIF: Challenging	OBJ: Interpretation
8. ANS: C	DIF: Challenging	OBJ: Interpretation
9. ANS: B	DIF: Challenging	OBJ: Literary Analysis
10. ANS: D	DIF: Average	OBJ: Interpretation
11. ANS: D	DIF: Average	OBJ: Comprehension
12. ANS: B	DIF: Challenging	OBJ: Interpretation
13. ANS: A	DIF: Average	OBJ: Literary Analysis
14. ANS: B	DIF: Average	OBJ: Literary Analysis
15. ANS: C	DIF: Challenging	OBJ: Interpretation
16. ANS: A	DIF: Average	OBJ: Literary Analysis
17. ANS: A	DIF: Challenging	OBJ: Interpretation
18. ANS: D	DIF: Average	OBJ: Literary Analysis

Vocabulary

19. ANS: B	DIF: Average	OBJ: Vocabulary
20. ANS: C	DIF: Average	OBJ: Vocabulary

Essay

21. Students should respond that "Fear" illustrates maternal or motherly love and expresses the idea that it is painful for mothers to imagine letting go of their children. They should respond that "The Bean Eaters" illustrates old, married love and expresses the idea that after many years, a couple's truest treasures are their memories. Students should respond that "La Belle Dame sans Merci" illustrates young, romantic love (or infatuation) and expresses the idea that this type of love rarely lasts and is often disappointing.

Difficulty: *Average*
Objective: *Essay*

22. Students might imagine Mistral speaking soothingly and reassuringly to the mother in an attempt to calm her fears; Brooks speaking respectfully and gratefully to the old couple, perhaps thanking them for the lesson they have taught her about love; and Keats speaking calmly but objectively to the knight in an attempt to pull him back into "reality." Accept all reasonable responses.

Difficulty: *Average*
Objective: *Essay*

23. Students may identify the mood of "Fear" as anxious or fearful and the mood of "La Belle Dame sans Merci" as romantic, dreamy, or magical. They will likely conclude that details such as the bird nesting in the eave, a secluded queen, and a mother rocking her child help create the mood of "Fear" and that the distant setting, the natural and magical details, and the romantic characters help create the mood of "La Belle Dame sans Merci." Accept other reasonable answers. Students may feel that the mood of Keats's poem is more distinct because it is expressed in virtually every aspect of the poem.

Difficulty: *Challenging*
Objective: *Essay*

Writing Workshop Unit 4, Part 1

Descriptive Essay: Integrating Grammar Skills, p. 100

A. 1. around the corner; 2. beside the house; 3. for over fifty years; 4. like clockwork (*or* like clockwork nearly every October 1)

B. Sample Paragraph

At 3 P.M. the school day ended. The children then often played together. On warm spring days, they enjoyed Columbus Park. Younger children liked the swings and slides. Beyond the children's playground, teenagers played ball or jogged. Some even went boating.

Unit 4, Part 1 Answers

Benchmark Test 7, p. 101

MULTIPLE CHOICE

1. ANS: C
2. ANS: B
3. ANS: C
4. ANS: C
5. ANS: D
6. ANS: B
7. ANS: A
8. ANS: D
9. ANS: A
10. ANS: B

11. ANS: D

12. ANS: B

13. ANS: B

14. ANS: B

15. ANS: C

16. ANS: A

17. ANS: D

18. ANS: B

19. ANS: C A

20. ANS: A

21. ANS: A

22. ANS: D

23. ANS: A

24. ANS: D

25. ANS: B

26. ANS: A

27. ANS: B

28. ANS: D

29. ANS: B

30. ANS: C

ESSAY

31. Students should adopt the personality of something nonhuman and express the feelings and ideas that they imagine such a speaker might express if it were human. Poems may use meter and rhyme or may be written in free verse.

32. Students should write a five-line poem in which the first and third lines contain five syllables and the other lines contain seven syllables. The tanka should focus on a single strong image or idea.

33. Students should use precise words that create a strong impression. They should include sensory details that appeal to several senses, not just the sense of sight. They might also include figurative language, such as personification, simile, and metaphor. Ideal essays should follow a logical organization and be free of errors in grammar.

Unit 4, Part 2 Answers

Diagnostic Test 8, p. 108

MULTIPLE CHOICE

1. ANS: C

2. ANS: D

3. ANS: A

4. ANS: A

5. ANS: C

6. ANS: D

7. ANS: B

8. ANS: B

9. ANS: C

10. ANS: A

11. ANS: B

12. ANS: D

13. ANS: A

14. ANS: D

15. ANS: C

Poetry Collection: Yusef Komunyakaa, Eve Merriam, and Emily Dickinson

Vocabulary Warm-up Exercises, p. 112

A. 1. survive
2. superior
3. flitting
4. makeshift
5. impossible
6. numerous

B. Sample Answers

1. She sang the final note waveringly with her *tremulous* voice.

2. A *metaphor* compares two things without using the words "like" or "as."

3. Consumers found the solid product *superior* to its flimsier competition.

4. The new *residence* on Tenth Street will be someone's home.

5. When the magician *conjured* my own scarf, I gasped in amazement.

Reading Warm-up A, p. 113

Sample Answers

1. to make their living as athletes; *Impossible* means "not able to be done or to happen."

2. Numerous options are available to someone who is interested in becoming involved in sports. *Many* choices are open to a person who wants to participate in a sport.

3. (Some adult leagues); *Makeshift* means "temporary, provisional."

4. All are focused on playing at the top of their chosen sport. *Flitting* means "moving quickly from one place to another."

5. in helping a person to maintain fitness and health; I think that reading is *superior* to television-watching as a form of recreation.

6. the tedium of the average workweek; *Survive* means "to continue to live normally, despite difficulties."

Unit 4 Resources: Poetry

© Pearson Education, Inc., publishing as Pearson Prentice Hall. All rights reserved.

218

Reading Warm-up B, p. 114

Sample Answers

1. <u>A metaphor makes a comparison between two seemingly unrelated things—such as "my love is a rose" or "their residence is a hornet's nest."</u> My heart is an open book.

2. The metaphor compares a *residence* to a hornet's nest. Their house is a noisy, unpleasant place.

3. *Face* is a synonym for *countenance*. An unwelcoming *countenance* might be unsmiling, glaring, and severe.

4. A *raconteur* might tell jokes, relate anecdotes, imitate other people, and tell amusing or instructive stories. My friend Steve is a *raconteur* who regales us with stories of his travels.

5. (song); The violin made a beautiful, *tremulous* sound.

6. (rabbit); The magician *conjured* a bouquet of flowers in front of my eyes.

Poetry Collection: Yusef Komunyakaa, Eve Merriam, and Emily Dickinson

Literary Analysis: Figurative Language, p. 115

Sample Answers

A. Simile: "The Wind—tapped like a tired Man"; "His Speech was like the Push / Of numerous Humming Birds"

Metaphor: "Morning is / a new sheet of paper"; "They were all Jackie Robinson / & Willie Mays"

Personification: "night folds it up"; "The Wind—tapped like a tired Man"

B. Flower: daffodil

Simile: The daffodil was as yellow as the yolk of an egg.

Metaphor: The daffodils were tiny suns peeking out at the world.

Personification: The daffodils swayed, a choir rocking to the rhythm of the wind.

Reading: Picture Imagery to Paraphrase Poems, p. 116

Sample Answers

1. Image: Women wearing flowered skirts

   Paraphrase: The heat on Sunday afternoon grew intense.

2. Image: Two groups of words: one "bright" and happy, one "dark" and grim

   Paraphrase: The good events and the bad events of the day are gone.

3. Image: A hostess offering her guest a chair.

   Paraphrase: Because wind is as formless as air, it could not sit in a chair.

Vocabulary Builder, p. 117

A. Sample Answers

1. the last leaf on a tree; the hand of a ninety-year-old man; a frightened child's voice

2. Benjamin Franklin's face on the hundred-dollar bill; four presidents' faces carved in stone at Mt. Rushmore; the *Mona Lisa*

B. Sample Answers

1. The president's grim countenance hinted at bad news to come.

   Principal Jamison's calm countenance reassured the students.

2. In a tremulous voice, Vicki asked if they were lost.

   Grandmother passed me the journal with tremulous hands.

C. 1. C; 2. B

Enrichment: Baseball Greats, p. 120

Students should provide accurate biographical information on the baseball player of their choice. The biographical sketch should focus on the player's baseball career.

Selection Test A, p. 121

Critical Reading

1. ANS: B	DIF: Easy	OBJ: Comprehension
2. ANS: C	DIF: Easy	OBJ: Reading
3. ANS: C	DIF: Easy	OBJ: Literary Analysis
4. ANS: B	DIF: Easy	OBJ: Literary Analysis
5. ANS: A	DIF: Easy	OBJ: Interpretation
6. ANS: B	DIF: Easy	OBJ: Literary Analysis
7. ANS: B	DIF: Easy	OBJ: Reading
8. ANS: B	DIF: Easy	OBJ: Comprehension
9. ANS: A	DIF: Easy	OBJ: Comprehension
10. ANS: C	DIF: Easy	OBJ: Interpretation
11. ANS: B	DIF: Easy	OBJ: Reading
12. ANS: C	DIF: Easy	OBJ: Interpretation

Vocabulary and Grammar

13. ANS: B	DIF: Easy	OBJ: Vocabulary
14. ANS: B	DIF: Easy	OBJ: Vocabulary
15. ANS: D	DIF: Easy	OBJ: Grammar

Essay

16. In their essays, students should explain that the poem describes a Sunday baseball game. The players are young men, cheered on by their wives and children. Komunyakaa compares the players to great African

American ballplayers, to cats, and to magicians in order to emphasize their skill and their love of the game. The baseball games give the players a chance to escape and forget about their worries.

Difficulty: *Easy*
Objective: *Essay*

17. In their essays, students should point out that "Metaphor" presents a metaphor in which morning is compared to a blank sheet of paper. Each morning presents a blank sheet of paper on which a person can "write" the events and experiences of the day. Each night, the day's experiences are folded up and filed away. With this metaphor, Merriam is saying that each morning presents a new beginning. In "The Wind—tapped like a tired Man," the wind is compared to a tired man. The speaker sees the wind as a force of nature having a personality and a will of its own. The poet uses the metaphor to show how important it is to appreciate small moments such as a simple gust of wind blowing through a house.

Difficulty: *Easy*
Objective: *Essay*

Selection Test B, p. 124

Critical Reading

1. ANS: D	DIF: Average	OBJ: Comprehension
2. ANS: C	DIF: Average	OBJ: Literary Analysis
3. ANS: D	DIF: Challenging	OBJ: Interpretation
4. ANS: C	DIF: Average	OBJ: Reading
5. ANS: A	DIF: Challenging	OBJ: Interpretation
6. ANS: C	DIF: Challenging	OBJ: Reading
7. ANS: A	DIF: Average	OBJ: Interpretation
8. ANS: B	DIF: Average	OBJ: Literary Analysis
9. ANS: B	DIF: Average	OBJ: Comprehension
10. ANS: C	DIF: Challenging	OBJ: Literary Analysis
11. ANS: A	DIF: Average	OBJ: Interpretation
12. ANS: A	DIF: Average	OBJ: Reading
13. ANS: A	DIF: Average	OBJ: Comprehension

Vocabulary and Grammar

14. ANS: B	DIF: Average	OBJ: Vocabulary
15. ANS: A	DIF: Average	OBJ: Vocabulary
16. ANS: D	DIF: Average	OBJ: Vocabulary
17. ANS: C	DIF: Average	OBJ: Grammar
18. ANS: D	DIF: Challenging	OBJ: Grammar

Essay

19. In their essays, students should note that the wind moves rapidly and in an agitated manner in the speaker's house. The wind is personified as a male visitor—it is compared to a tired man and to a timid man—who thinks he might want to stay, but then chooses to leave. The speaker treats the wind as if he were a guest who keeps her company. The visitor then leaves the speaker alone, just as she was in the beginning.

Difficulty: *Average*
Objective: *Essay*

20. In their essays, students should describe the event in "The Wind—tapped like a tired Man" as a woman letting the wind into her house. It flies around, agitating the curtains and making a delicate noise, and then it leaves as quickly as it came. The event depicted in "Glory" is a Sunday baseball game. A group of young men play baseball, while their wives and children watch them. They play hard and with great spirit, for the game gives them a chance to forget about their worries.

Difficulty: *Average*
Objective: *Essay*

Poetry Collection: Edna St. Vincent Millay, Dahlia Ravikovitch, and Emily Dickinson

Vocabulary Warm-up Exercises, p. 128

A. 1. haste
2. motionless
3. overcome
4. gradually
5. shatter
6. superb

B. Sample Answers

1. A. We took a new *route* to school this morning.
   B. Traffic was *rerouted* to avoid a flooded section of the highway.

2. A. If someone is an *objector*, he or she disagrees with a policy or rule.
   B. I *object* to the use of commercials in children's television.

3. A. The soft song *eased* the minds of the worried listeners.
   B. The beautiful melody brought me *ease* and confidence.

4. A. I have been very *conscientious* about flossing my teeth.
   B. The dentist said she could tell that I have been flossing *conscientiously*.

5. A. The jockey *cinches* the belt to hold his horse's saddle on snugly.
   B. The belt was *cinched* so tightly that the horse had trouble breathing.

Reading Warm-up A, p. 129

Sample Answers

1. holding the same position day and night; The moon appears to be *motionless*, but it actually orbits Earth.

2. this boulder's weighty pride; *Overcome* means "to defeat or conquer."

3. weathering and erosion; I might learn a new language *gradually*.

4. (patient); *Haste* means "in a great hurry."

5. <u>When the conditions are right for ice wedging, a few seconds are all it takes</u>. The view of the Grand Canyon from the rim is *superb*.

6. <u>It will break apart into two or more pieces</u>. A pane of glass will *shatter* if it is hit by a ball.

Reading Warm-up B, p. 130

Sample Answers

1. (calmed); *Eased* means "calmed or made less nervous."

2. <u>in poor health</u>; Not all illnesses have visible symptoms, so you cannot identify an *infirm* person by sight alone.

3. <u>carefully selects the best poems for each patient</u>; A witness must be extremely *conscientious* during a trial.

4. <u>refuse to read poetry at all</u>; An *objector* is a person who objects to or disagrees with something.

5. (path); The *route* I take follows Main Street from Dryden Avenue until we reach Oakland Parkway and turn right.

6. (a wide waist); *Cinches* means "tightens using force."

Poetry Collection: Edna St. Vincent Millay, Dahlia Ravikovitch, and Emily Dickinson

Literary Analysis: Figurative Language, p. 131

Sample Answers

A. Simile: "The Truth's superb surprise / As Lightning to the Children eased"

Metaphor: "Till a little seal comes to rub against them"; "Am I a spy in the land of the living, that I should deliver men to Death?"

Personification: "For years they lie on their backs"; "I hear him leading his horse out of the stall"

B. Animal: giraffe

Simile: The giraffe was as tall as a skyscraper.

Metaphor: The giraffe's neck was a snake reaching to the heights of the trees.

Personification: The giraffe swayed over to our group, flirting with her great brown eyes.

Reading: Picture Imagery to Paraphrase Poems, p. 132

Sample Answers

1. Image: A person preparing to ride a horse

Paraphrase: Millay refuses to help Death.

2. Image: A rock staying perfectly still

Paraphrase: Rocks, like people, hide their injuries.

3. Image: A bright light

Paraphrase: The truth should be toned down to avoid hurting people.

Vocabulary Builder, p. 133

A. Sample Answers

1. a garden in summer; a child who discovers a new talent; a company that is doing well

2. the Earth's orbit of the sun; a trip around the world; a race around a track

B. Sample Answers

1. The rose garden flourishes if the weather is hot and sunny.

When Martin is put in a different classroom from his twin brother, he flourishes.

2. The race cars made several circuits of the track at incredible speeds.

We made a complete circuit of the mall before deciding on a purchase.

C. 1. D; 2. A

Enrichment: The Sun, p. 136

A. Students should be encouraged to notice the changes in the sun's intensity from early morning to evening. They should be able to observe that the sun seems strongest at midday, when it appears most directly overhead in the sky. Students should note the weather conditions and how they affect the intensity of the sunlight.

B. Sample Answers

1. The sun changes positions in the Earth's atmosphere, and in the process, its light changes in intensity. Sunlight is most intense when it is directly overhead. When it appears to be lower in the earth's atmosphere, it is not as intense. By using the word *slant*, the poet wants people to realize that truth is easier to face and less intense when it is not faced directly.

2. The lines indicate that looking into the sun, like looking directly at the truth, can "dazzle" and result in blindness. The blindness that Dickinson refers to is an emotional state.

Poetry Collections: Yusef Komunyakaa, Eve Merriam, and Emily Dickinson; Edna St. Vincent Millay, Dahlia Ravikovitch, and Emily Dickinson

Build Language Skills: Vocabulary Skill, p. 137

A. Sample Answers

1. theorize   Scientists theorize about the results of their experiments.

2. characterize   I would characterize my sister as a happy person.

3. dramatize   In class, we will dramatize a story by Edgar Allan Poe.

B. Sample Answers

1. A person might want to study psychology to learn about the human mind and emotions.
2. The illness is unlikely to recur because once you have had the chicken pox, you become immune.
3. Political ads sometimes distort an opponent's ideas in order to hurt his or her credibility.
4. The most drastic weather event I have ever experienced was a tornado that came through our town.
5. It is important not to minimize the time you need to finish a project because things are often more complicated than they seem at first.

Build Language Skills: Grammar, p. 138

A. 1. adverb; on the ballfield
2. adverb; to a tired man
3. adverb; to Death
4. adjective; in the poem
5. adverb; to the listener
6. adjective; in the third verse
7. adverb; against the rocks
8. adverb; at the speaker

B. Sample Answers

1. The "glory" <u>in the ballplayers' lives</u> is baseball.
2. Each morning brings a new chance <u>for each person</u>.
3. Death rides <u>on horseback</u>, collecting his victims.
4. The rocks bake <u>in the sun</u>.

Poetry Collection: Edna St. Vincent Millay, Dahlia Ravikovitch, and Emily Dickinson

Selection Test A, p. 139

Critical Reading

1. ANS: D	DIF: Easy	OBJ: Comprehension
2. ANS: A	DIF: Easy	OBJ: Interpretation
3. ANS: B	DIF: Easy	OBJ: Literary Analysis
4. ANS: D	DIF: Easy	OBJ: Reading
5. ANS: B	DIF: Easy	OBJ: Interpretation
6. ANS: B	DIF: Easy	OBJ: Literary Analysis
7. ANS: C	DIF: Easy	OBJ: Comprehension
8. ANS: D	DIF: Easy	OBJ: Literary Analysis
9. ANS: B	DIF: Easy	OBJ: Comprehension
10. ANS: C	DIF: Easy	OBJ: Reading
11. ANS: A	DIF: Easy	OBJ: Literary Analysis

Vocabulary and Grammar

12. ANS: C	DIF: Easy	OBJ: Vocabulary
13. ANS: A	DIF: Easy	OBJ: Vocabulary
14. ANS: C	DIF: Easy	OBJ: Grammar
15. ANS: A	DIF: Easy	OBJ: Grammar

Essay

16. In their essays, students should note that Dickinson compares truth to light. She states that when told at a "slant," the truth can illuminate, but when told too harshly, truth can blind. Students should note that Dickinson feels too much truth can be damaging, but when told with compassion and feeling, it can create light from darkness.
    Difficulty: *Easy*
    Objective: *Essay*

17. In their essays, students should focus on one of the two poems. If students choose "Conscientious Objector," they should point out that the poem's message is that a person should not give in to death. Images of death as a military agent of destruction help to create and strengthen this message. In "Pride," the poem's message is that when people hide their hurt out of pride, they eventually will crack. Ravikovitch supports her message with images of rocks as they are tossed by waves, frozen, lying in wait for years, and finally rubbed against by a seal.
    Difficulty: *Easy*
    Objective: *Essay*

Selection Test B, p. 142

Critical Reading

1. ANS: D	DIF: Average	OBJ: Comprehension
2. ANS: A	DIF: Average	OBJ: Interpretation
3. ANS: C	DIF: Challenging	OBJ: Interpretation
4. ANS: D	DIF: Average	OBJ: Interpretation
5. ANS: B	DIF: Challenging	OBJ: Reading
6. ANS: A	DIF: Average	OBJ: Literary Analysis
7. ANS: C	DIF: Challenging	OBJ: Literary Analysis
8. ANS: B	DIF: Average	OBJ: Comprehension
9. ANS: C	DIF: Challenging	OBJ: Interpretation
10. ANS: B	DIF: Average	OBJ: Reading
11. ANS: B	DIF: Challenging	OBJ: Literary Analysis
12. ANS: A	DIF: Challenging	OBJ: Reading
13. ANS: C	DIF: Average	OBJ: Interpretation
14. ANS: B	DIF: Average	OBJ: Comprehension
15. ANS: D	DIF: Average	OBJ: Literary Analysis

Vocabulary and Grammar

16. ANS: A	DIF: Average	OBJ: Vocabulary
17. ANS: C	DIF: Average	OBJ: Vocabulary
18. ANS: B	DIF: Average	OBJ: Vocabulary
19. ANS: B	DIF: Average	OBJ: Grammar
20. ANS: A	DIF: Average	OBJ: Grammar

Essay

21. In their essays, students should identify the message of the poem and support their points with examples from the poem. The message of "Pride" is that people hide their hurts and troubles until some event causes them to be uncovered. The poet supports her message by creating the metaphor of troubles as rocks that are baked and frozen by heat and cold, lying in wait for years, until they are finally cracked by the touch of a little seal. Students' opinions of the poet's success will vary.

    Difficulty: *Average*

    Objective: *Essay*

22. In their essays, students should point out that Dickinson feels that for the truth to be accepted and understood, it must be told at a "slant" and must "dazzle gradually." She feels that truth must be introduced gradually and with kindness or people will be unable to comprehend and accept it. Dickinson's metaphor of the truth as light supports this idea: Without a gradual explanation, the truth will "blind" people—it will be too harsh for them, and they will be unable to see it clearly.

    Difficulty: *Average*

    Objective: *Essay*

Poetry Collection: Langston Hughes, John McCrae, and Carl Sandburg

Vocabulary Warm-up Exercises, p. 146

A.
1. quarrel
2. weary
3. sob
4. croon
5. chords
6. mellow

B. Sample Answers
1. T; A club might help a person meet new friends and feel less *lonesome*.
2. F; Some *foes* are much more dangerous than others.
3. T; Feeling *drowsy* is a normal reaction to a long car ride.
4. F; If you are *amid* a field in bloom, you are in the middle of it, so you would see flowers.
5. F; Many *droning* sounds, such as the humming of a bee, are quite soft.
6. F; If a shout *echoed* loudly, anyone nearby could have heard it.

Reading Warm-up A, p. 147

Sample Answers
1. the troubles they have seen; *Weary* means "tired of."
2. (groups of notes played together); A person can play many different *chords* on a piano.

3. in an elegant, beautiful voice; *Crooned* means "sang softly or sweetly."
4. burying the words under heartfelt tears; I might *sob* if I finished writing an essay but then accidentally erased the file.
5. If they fought their harsh treatment, they would face worse consequences. A *quarrel* is a fight or an argument about something.
6. (soft) (comforting); You can create a *mellow* mood by playing soft music, dimming the lights, and using candles.

Reading Warm-up B, p. 148

Sample Answers
1. the chaos and tragedy of World War I; *Amid* means "in the middle of."
2. (enemy); If someone is your *foe*, he or she acts against you.
3. (gunfire and rifle fire); I have heard the *droning* of jet engines at the airport.
4. without companions; I might feel *lonesome* if I were in strange city without my friends or family.
5. (at rest); I feel *drowsy* when I watch a boring movie late at night.
6. the dead; (in the minds of readers); The last line of the movie *echoed* in my head for many days.

Poetry Collection: Langston Hughes, John McCrae, and Carl Sandburg

Literary Analysis: Sound Devices, p. 149

Sample Answers

Alliteration: "the slippery sand-paper" from "Jazz Fantasia"; "Droning a drowsy" from "The Weary Blues"

Assonance: "sad raggy tune" from "The Weary Blues"; "The torch; be yours" from "In Flanders Fields"

Consonance: "In Flanders fields the poppies blow" from "In Flanders Fields"; "the rough stuff" from "Jazz Fantasia"

Onomatopoeia: "husha-husha-hush" from "Jazz Fantasia"; "Thump, thump, thump" from "The Weary Blues"

Reading: Break Down Long Sentences to Paraphrase Poems, p. 150

Sample Answers
1. Who? a musician

   Action: played the blues

   Paraphrase: On Lenox Avenue the other night, under an old gas light, a musician swayed and played a blues song.
2. Who? dead soldiers

   Action: spoke of their lives

   Paraphrase: We were once alive and saw and felt life, but now we are dead on the battlefield.

3. Who? the jazzmen

   Action: played music gently

   Paraphrase: Stop playing roughly; listen to the steam-boat, see the lanterns and the stars, and watch the moon riding low as you keep playing.

Vocabulary Builder, p. 151

A. 1. ebony; 2. melancholy; 3. pallor

B. Sample Answers

1. The ebony lettering on the jazz club sign revealed that the group we wanted to hear was performing that night.
2. The words to the old gospel song were melancholy and moving.
3. Jeanine's pallor showed that she was still suffering from food poisoning.

C. 1. B; 2. A; 3. C

Enrichment: Jazz and Blues, p. 154

Students should have little difficulty finding both written and audio material for the listed artists. Students' choices of songs will vary. Students should note distinguishing characteristics of each song.

Selection Test A, p. 155

Critical Reading

1. ANS: C	DIF: Easy	OBJ: Interpretation
2. ANS: D	DIF: Easy	OBJ: Interpretation
3. ANS: C	DIF: Easy	OBJ: Comprehension
4. ANS: C	DIF: Easy	OBJ: Literary Analysis
5. ANS: A	DIF: Easy	OBJ: Reading
6. ANS: A	DIF: Easy	OBJ: Literary Analysis
7. ANS: B	DIF: Easy	OBJ: Comprehension
8. ANS: C	DIF: Easy	OBJ: Reading
9. ANS: D	DIF: Easy	OBJ: Reading
10. ANS: A	DIF: Easy	OBJ: Comprehension
11. ANS: B	DIF: Easy	OBJ: Literary Analysis
12. ANS: B	DIF: Easy	OBJ: Comprehension

Vocabulary and Grammar

13. ANS: A	DIF: Easy	OBJ: Vocabulary
14. ANS: B	DIF: Easy	OBJ: Vocabulary
15. ANS: B	DIF: Easy	OBJ: Grammar

Essay

16. In their essays, students should explain that the speakers of the poem are soldiers who have died on the battlefield and are buried in Flanders. The soldiers fought and perished in World War I. They are urging those still fighting and those at home to fight on in their cause and in their memory. Students should refer to details from

the poem that tell who, what, and where, such as the reference to "Flanders fields" and rows of "crosses" that "mark our place."

Difficulty: *Easy*

Objective: *Essay*

17. In their essays, students should discuss the use of alliteration, assonance, consonance, and onomatopoeia in the two poems and should point out examples of each. Examples include "Droning a drowsy" and "sad raggy tune" for alliteration and assonance in "The Weary Blues" and "the rough stuff" and "a hoo-hoo-hoo-oo" for consonance and onomatopoeia in "Jazz Fantasia." Students should note that the sound devices in "The Weary Blues" create a rhythm much like that of blues itself, syncopated and rhythmic. The sound devices in "Jazz Fantasia" create a less rhythmic, more improvisational feeling.

Difficulty: *Easy*

Objective: *Essay*

Selection Test B, p. 158

Critical Reading

1. ANS: B	DIF: Average	OBJ: Comprehension
2. ANS: A	DIF: Challenging	OBJ: Reading
3. ANS: C	DIF: Challenging	OBJ: Literary Analysis
4. ANS: B	DIF: Average	OBJ: Reading
5. ANS: B	DIF: Average	OBJ: Comprehension
6. ANS: C	DIF: Challenging	OBJ: Literary Analysis
7. ANS: D	DIF: Challenging	OBJ: Interpretation
8. ANS: C	DIF: Average	OBJ: Literary Analysis
9. ANS: A	DIF: Average	OBJ: Interpretation
10. ANS: B	DIF: Average	OBJ: Interpretation
11. ANS: C	DIF: Challenging	OBJ: Reading
12. ANS: A	DIF: Average	OBJ: Comprehension
13. ANS: B	DIF: Average	OBJ: Literary Analysis

Vocabulary and Grammar

14. ANS: B	DIF: Average	OBJ: Vocabulary
15. ANS: D	DIF: Average	OBJ: Vocabulary
16. ANS: D	DIF: Average	OBJ: Vocabulary
17. ANS: A	DIF: Challenging	OBJ: Grammar
18. ANS: A	DIF: Average	OBJ: Grammar
19. ANS: B	DIF: Average	OBJ: Grammar

Essay

20. In their essays, students should note that the rhythm and references in "Jazz Fantasia" suggest an appreciation of the art form. The references to drums, banjoes, tin pans, trombones, sand paper, traps, and horns show an appreciation of the many instruments and objects used to create sound in jazz. The use of adjectives such as

long, cool, winding, happy, slippery, and lonesome reflect the feel of jazz—as do the alliteration, assonance, consonance, and onomatopoeia in the poem. Students should include examples of sound devices such as "batter" for onomatopoeia, "slippery sand-paper" for alliteration, "happy tin pans" for assonance, and "the rough stuff" for consonance.

Difficulty: *Average*

Objective: *Essay*

21. In their essays, students should note that "In Flanders Fields" is about handing down a legacy—from the dead to the living. The soldiers who have been killed in battle challenge people still living to continue their fight. They say that if people who are living do not "carry the torch" and complete what has been started, they will be unable to rest peacefully. The successful handing down of this responsibility means that the speakers will be able to rest in peace.

Difficulty: *Average*

Objective: *Essay*

Poetry Collection: Alfred, Lord Tennyson; Robert Browning; and Jean Toomer

Vocabulary Warm-up Exercises, p. 162

A. 1. squealing
2. reapers
3. startled
4. pane
5. ringlets
6. wondrous

B. Sample Answers
1. You might need to wake up a *slumbering* person during an emergency, like a fire.
2. It would be very difficult to retrieve a quarter that fell down an *abysmal* well.
3. Researchers might use sonar or radar to find a shipwreck that has *lain* at the bottom of the ocean for many years.
4. The person can *continue* improving by practicing as often as possible.
5. Drinking lemonade is my favorite way to *quench* a thirst.

Reading Warm-up A, p. 163

Sample Answers
1. cut down and collected the tall wheat; *Reapers* are people who cut down or collect crops that are ripe.
2. (marvelous); I saw a *wondrous* sunrise at the beach.
3. had so carefully curled; Someone with hair in *ringlets* has hair that falls in long, tight curls.
4. a noise, a little tap that snapped me to life; My father was *startled* when my brothers sneaked up on him in the basement.

5. (glass); A *pane* is a sheet of glass, such as a window or the glass in a door.
6. (shrieking); *Squealing* means "making a high noise that sounds a little like a shriek or a whine."

Reading Warm-up B, p. 164

Sample Answers
1. at the bottom of the sea off the coast of Norway and Iceland; *Lain* means "rested."
2. (sleeping); You should not disturb a *slumbering* animal.
3. where it is almost impossible to study them; *Abysmal* means "very deep or too deep to measure."
4. When the tide went out, the squid was left in the open air and died. A *cove* might look like a bay, a coastal area surrounding water that leads into the sea or ocean.
5. (curiosity); I do not think scientists will *quench* their curiosity because no matter how much they learn, there will always be more questions to answer.
6. the hunt for the giant squid; I will *continue* playing basketball with our team for the rest of this school year.

Poetry Collection: Alfred, Lord Tennyson; Robert Browning; and Jean Toomer

Literary Analysis: Sound Devices, p. 165

Sample Answers

Alliteration: "sound of steel on stones" from "Reapers"; "large and low" from "Meeting at Night"

Assonance: "sea-scented beach" from "Meeting at Night"; "dreamless, uninvaded sleep" from "The Kraken"

Consonance: "grot and secret" from "The Kraken"; "spurt of a lighted" from "Meeting at Night"

Onomatopoeia: "tap" from "Meeting at Night"; "squealing" from "Reapers"

Reading: Break Down Long Sentences to Paraphrase Poems, p. 166

Sample Answers
1. Who? the Kraken
   Action: sleeps until the Apocalypse comes
   Paraphrase: The Kraken sleeps under the sea until the Apocalypse arrives, and then he will rise to the surface and die.
2. Who? the speaker
   Action: travels to meet his lover
   Paraphrase: The speaker crosses the beach and three fields and taps at the window of his lover, who lights a match.
3. Who? horses; a rat
   Action: pull a mower; bleeds
   Paraphrase: A mower drawn by horses moves through the field, cutting a field rat.

Vocabulary Builder, p. 167

A. 1. slumbering; 2. prow; 3. millennial

B. Sample Answers

1. Many local people attended Castle Craigan's millennial celebration.

2. The carved wooden figure of a beautiful woman jutted out from the prow of the ship.

3. The slumbering bears will not wake until spring arrives.

C. 1. D; 2. C; 3. B

Enrichment: Art and Poetry, p. 170

A. Sample Answers

For "The Kraken," students might mention details of the monster's position in the water, the sea life that surrounds him, or the monster eating sea worms. For "Meeting at Night," students might mention the wet sand, the man walking across the fields to the farmhouse, or the lighting of a match. For "Reapers," students might mention the scythes, the reapers sharpening their tools, or the field rat.

B. Designs will vary, but students should use details from the chart for inspiration.

Poetry Collections: Langston Hughes, John McCrae, and Carl Sandburg; Alfred, Lord Tennyson; Robert Browning; and Jean Toomer

Build Language Skills: Vocabulary Skill, p. 171

A. Sample Answers

1. No, psychology is the study of the human mind and emotions.

2. Yes, a dramatic person wants to perform.

3. Yes, someone who feels civic responsibility wants to help his or her community.

4. The activity of someone whose field is Egyptology would be studying Egypt (or Ancient Egypt).

5. If a friend were acting in an idiotic way, he or she would be acting in a stupid way, so I would urge him or her to stop.

B. Sample Answers

1. I have a nightmare about falling that seems to recur often.

2. Melissa tried to minimize the importance of the tryouts so she would not feel so nervous.

3. Troy's anger at Will served to distort his face into a mask of fury.

4. The main character was a psychology major who thought she could analyze anyone.

5. Tanya wanted to make a drastic change in her look by buying new, more stylish clothes.

Build Language Skills: Grammar, p. 172

A. 1. adverb; to re-create

2. noun; to make

3. adjective; to continue

4. noun; To make

B. Sample Answers

1. The soldiers in "In Flanders Fields" ask us to fight for them.

2. Sandburg's poem makes one want to play a musical instrument.

3. "Weary Blues" gives a sense of what it is like to sing the blues.

4. The soldiers in "In Flanders Fields" just want to rest in peace.

Poetry Collection: Alfred, Lord Tennyson; Robert Browning; and Jean Toomer

Selection Test A, p. 173

Critical Reading

1. ANS: C	DIF: Easy	OBJ: Comprehension
2. ANS: D	DIF: Easy	OBJ: Comprehension
3. ANS: A	DIF: Easy	OBJ: Literary Analysis
4. ANS: C	DIF: Easy	OBJ: Reading
5. ANS: B	DIF: Easy	OBJ: Comprehension
6. ANS: B	DIF: Easy	OBJ: Interpretation
7. ANS: A	DIF: Easy	OBJ: Literary Analysis
8. ANS: C	DIF: Easy	OBJ: Reading
9. ANS: A	DIF: Easy	OBJ: Interpretation
10. ANS: D	DIF: Easy	OBJ: Comprehension
11. ANS: C	DIF: Easy	OBJ: Reading
12. ANS: C	DIF: Easy	OBJ: Literary Analysis

Vocabulary and Grammar

13. ANS: D	DIF: Easy	OBJ: Vocabulary
14. ANS: D	DIF: Easy	OBJ: Vocabulary
15. ANS: B	DIF: Easy	OBJ: Grammar

Essay

16. In their essays, students should explain that the speaker has been on a journey at sea. He brings his boat to shore, walks through fields, and approaches a farmhouse where he eagerly taps on the window. The speaker's feelings on meeting the person inside the farmhouse are revealed by his description of their two beating hearts, which overpower voices expressing joy and fear.

Difficulty: *Easy*

Objective: *Essay*

17. In their essays, students should focus on one image and explain why it is effective. For example, they might mention the vivid images of the Kraken, explaining how those images helped them view a sea monster in a unique way; they may describe the image of the struck match in "Meeting at Night," explaining that the image helped them imagine the passion of the meeting; or they might discuss the image of the field rat, which reflects how nature can become the victim of progress.

Difficulty: *Easy*
Objective: *Essay*

Selection Test B, p. 176

Critical Reading

1. ANS: B	DIF: Average	OBJ: Literary Analysis
2. ANS: C	DIF: Challenging	OBJ: Reading
3. ANS: D	DIF: Challenging	OBJ: Literary Analysis
4. ANS: A	DIF: Average	OBJ: Comprehension
5. ANS: C	DIF: Average	OBJ: Comprehension
6. ANS: D	DIF: Challenging	OBJ: Literary Analysis
7. ANS: B	DIF: Average	OBJ: Reading
8. ANS: C	DIF: Average	OBJ: Comprehension
9. ANS: C	DIF: Challenging	OBJ: Interpretation
10. ANS: B	DIF: Average	OBJ: Interpretation
11. ANS: A	DIF: Challenging	OBJ: Interpretation
12. ANS: B	DIF: Average	OBJ: Interpretation
13. ANS: C	DIF: Challenging	OBJ: Literary Analysis
14. ANS: C	DIF: Average	OBJ: Reading

Vocabulary and Grammar

15. ANS: B	DIF: Average	OBJ: Vocabulary
16. ANS: C	DIF: Average	OBJ: Vocabulary
17. ANS: C	DIF: Average	OBJ: Vocabulary
18. ANS: D	DIF: Average	OBJ: Grammar

Essay

19. In their essays, students should note that in "The Kraken," the use of the *s* suggests a state of slumber and also brings to mind the hissing of the monster that lives beneath the sea. Students may use the following words as examples: *sea, sleep, sunlight, shadowy sides, swell, sponges, sickly, secret cell, slumbering, seaworms, seen,* and *surface.* In "Reapers," the *s* creates the sound of the scythes cutting through the weeds. Examples include *sound, steel, stones, sharpening scythes, start, silent, swinging, startled,* and *squealing.*

Difficulty: *Average*
Objective: *Essay*

20. In their essays, students should tell the stories of the poems. "The Kraken" is the story of a legendary sea monster that has lived and slept for centuries under the sea.

At the time of the apocalypse, the Kraken will awaken, come to the surface of the sea, and then die. "Meeting at Night" tells the story of the speaker's nighttime journey across the water, a beach, and fields to the house where his beloved waits for him. Students should include references to specific words and phrases from the poem.

Difficulty: *Average*
Objective: *Essay*

Poetry by Bei Dao, Shu Ting, Emily Dickinson, and Emily Brontë

Vocabulary Warm-up Exercises, p. 180

A.
1. liberty
2. encounter
3. esteem
4. affection
5. disaster
6. fated

B. Sample Answers
1. The *desolate* city had low employment and few people.
2. I will only *implore* you to do something if I really care about the outcome.
3. We learned our lines by *repetition* after reciting them countless times.
4. The contractors had *trodden* over our vegetable garden, so we had a small harvest.
5. The rain *vanished* at noon, and the sun shone brightly until nightfall.

Reading Warm-up A, p. 181

Sample Answers
1. (freedom); The oppressed people longed for *liberty*.
2. Maria and Elizabeth both died of the disease that had killed their mother; A *disaster* is "a sudden event that causes great harm or damage."
3. they wrote a collection of poems together; *Encounter* means "an occasion when one meets or experiences something."
4. (*Jane Eyre*); *Esteem* is "a feeling of high regard and admiration."
5. (love); *Affection* is "a feeling of gentle love and caring."
6. die young; The couple felt that their first meeting was *fated*.

Reading Warm-up B, p. 182

Sample Answers
1. It would be surprising to find a city in a *barren* desert because food would not grow there easily. *Fertile* is an antonym for *barren*.
2. the Earth; *Vanished* means "having disappeared suddenly, especially in a way that cannot be easily explained."

3. I would expect to find few people in a *desolate* region because it would be stark and deserted. *Thriving* is an antonym for *desolate*.

4. (underfoot); If artifacts had been *trodden* over, or walked over, I would expect them to be somewhat damaged.

5. <u>to fund a full-scale expedition</u>; I would *beg* someone to help my family if they were in need.

6. Through *repetition* of the same mistake, I learned that people feel it is insensitive to be late to appointments. *Repetition* means "the act of doing again and again."

Poetry by Bei Dao, Shu Ting, Emily Dickinson, and Emily Brontë

Literary Analysis: Theme, p. 183

Sample Answers

1. A. an endless beginning, a search for what vanishes, grave joys, tearless griefs, hope hedged with doubt, faith drowned in lamentation
   B. that human actions are futile or useless; that they will inevitably lead to grief or death

2. Life is not meaningless; human actions should be guided by hope.

3. A. those who never succeed
   B. Dwelling on what you cannot have will only cause you more pain. If you meet with success, do not take it for granted.

4. A. freedom and courage
   B. I agree because true success is the freedom to become who you want to be. I disagree because riches and fame can sometimes help a person find personal fulfillment.

Vocabulary Builder, p. 184

Sample Answers

A. 1. false, because watering plants makes them healthy
   2. true, because the person might see how important the favor is to you
   3. false, because there is usually great celebration after a great victory;
      true, because the losing party may wail or cry
   4. false, because a magnifying glass cannot help you hear a bird's melodies

B. 1. C; 2. A; 3. D; 4. C

Selection Test A, p. 186

Critical Reading

1. ANS: A	DIF: Easy	OBJ: Interpretation
2. ANS: D	DIF: Easy	OBJ: Literary Analysis
3. ANS: B	DIF: Easy	OBJ: Literary Analysis
4. ANS: C	DIF: Easy	OBJ: Interpretation
5. ANS: B	DIF: Easy	OBJ: Comprehension
6. ANS: C	DIF: Easy	OBJ: Comprehension

7. ANS: A	DIF: Easy	OBJ: Interpretation
8. ANS: D	DIF: Easy	OBJ: Literary Analysis
9. ANS: B	DIF: Easy	OBJ: Comprehension
10. ANS: B	DIF: Easy	OBJ: Comprehension
11. ANS: C	DIF: Easy	OBJ: Interpretation
12. ANS: A	DIF: Easy	OBJ: Literary Analysis
13. ANS: B	DIF: Easy	OBJ: Comprehension
14. ANS: D	DIF: Easy	OBJ: Interpretation

Vocabulary

15. ANS: A	DIF: Easy	OBJ: Vocabulary

Essay

16. Students should choose three of the four poems and explain how the poem answers the question. For "All," students might answer no, because death and nothingness will ultimately win out. For "Also All," students might answer yes, because by having hope and making good choices, we can create a better world. For "Success is counted sweetest," students might answer no, because failure can come to you even if you try to succeed. They may answer yes, because if we learn not to pine for success, we may find true happiness. For "The Old Stoic," students might answer yes, because if human beings value the treasures of the soul rather than the treasures of the world, they may overcome death.
    Difficulty: *Easy*
    Objective: *Essay*

17. Students may respond that the speaker of "All" would value courage because it would help a person face the bleak reality of death and that the speaker of "Also All" would value courage because it would help a person carry the heavy burden of hope. Students may say that the speaker of "Also All" would value courage more because in her view, there is more at stake—namely, a better future. Students may say that the speaker of "All" may value courage less because in his view, everything eventually comes to nothing. Accept all other reasonable responses.
    Difficulty: *Easy*
    Objective: *Essay*

Selection Test B, p. 189

Critical Reading

1. ANS: D	DIF: Average	OBJ: Interpretation
2. ANS: A	DIF: Average	OBJ: Interpretation
3. ANS: C	DIF: Average	OBJ: Literary Analysis
4. ANS: B	DIF: Challenging	OBJ: Interpretation
5. ANS: B	DIF: Challenging	OBJ: Literary Analysis
6. ANS: A	DIF: Average	OBJ: Interpretation
7. ANS: D	DIF: Average	OBJ: Comprehension
8. ANS: C	DIF: Average	OBJ: Comprehension

9. ANS: B	DIF: Challenging	OBJ: Interpretation
10. ANS: A	DIF: Average	OBJ: Interpretation
11. ANS: C	DIF: Average	OBJ: Interpretation
12. ANS: D	DIF: Challenging	OBJ: Comprehension
13. ANS: B	DIF: Average	OBJ: Comprehension
14. ANS: A	DIF: Average	OBJ: Literary Analysis
15. ANS: D	DIF: Average	OBJ: Comprehension
16. ANS: A	DIF: Average	OBJ: Literary Analysis
17. ANS: A	DIF: Challenging	OBJ: Literary Analysis
18. ANS: D	DIF: Challenging	OBJ: Interpretation

Vocabulary

19. ANS: B	DIF: Average	OBJ: Vocabulary
20. ANS: C	DIF: Average	OBJ: Vocabulary

Essay

21. Students should respond that the poems "Also All" and "The Old Stoic" express a form of the idea "Hope is essential" and that the poems "All" and "Success is counted sweetest" express a form of the idea "Hope is pointless." Extended ideas will vary, but they may resemble the following: "Also All"—hope is essential to build a better tomorrow for humanity; "The Old Stoic"—hope is essential to attain true freedom; "All"—hope is pointless because all will end in death (or tragedy); and "Success is counted sweetest"—hope is pointless because defeat or failure is much more common than success. Some students may conclude that Dickinson's poem expresses neither idea, but rather is an observation about the nature of failure.
Difficulty: *Average*
Objective: *Essay*

22. Students should identify at least one image from each of two poems that they have selected and explain how this image relates to the poem's theme. For "All," students may cite the image of an explosion followed by stillness. This image helps express the theme that everything comes to nothingness. For "Also All," students may cite the image of hope as a burden being shouldered. This image helps express the theme that even though much of life is bleak, hope may lead us to a better future. For "Success is counted sweetest," students may cite the image of a dying soldier who longs for victory. This image helps convey the theme that success is most highly prized by those who never attain it.
Difficulty: *Average*
Objective: *Essay*

23. Students may respond that "All" expresses the conflict or paradox that all joy leads to grief or that all life leads to death. The poet offers no resolution for this conflict because he believes that no resolution is possible. Students may respond that "Also All" expresses the contradiction that hope is a burden. The resolution to this conflict lies in hope itself—in the gradual movement

toward a better tomorrow. Students may respond that "Success is counted sweetest" expresses the contradiction or irony that success is valued most by those who never attain it. The poet does not directly offer a resolution for this contradiction, although she may imply that a person may be happier if he or she does not pine for success. Students may respond that "The Old Stoic" expresses the conflict between worldly "successes" and the speaker's own values of freedom and courage. The poet implies that the resolution to this conflict is to abandon one's pursuit of worldly success and seek other kinds of fulfillment.
Difficulty: *Challenging*
Objective: *Essay*

Writing Workshop—Unit 4, Part 2

Analytic Response to Literature: Integrating Grammar Skills, p. 193

A. 1. among; 2. between; 3. like; 4. as
B. 1. We watched the boat race between Rolf and Ian.
2. Rolf rowed as if he had a lot of practice.
3. correct
4. Both of them zipped along, just as I expected.
5. Among the dozens of other competitions, there was none as exciting.

Spelling Workshop—Unit 4

Words with Similar Endings, p. 194

A. 1. disguise; 2. supervised; 3. paradise; 4. plagiarize; 5. treatise; 6. improvise; 7. jeopardize; 8. paralyzed; 9. exercise; 10. commercialize
B. 1. **Phrase:** the teacher supervised the students. **Sample paragraph:** The teacher closely *supervised* the students as they wrote the papers. He explained to them the importance of using their own words in order to never *plagiarize*. Many of the students became *paralyzed* with fear over the idea of getting in trouble for copying.
2. **Phrase:** could improvise a new ending. **Sample paragraph:** The actors, wearing their *disguises*, decided to *improvise* a new ending to the play. The director, however, feared that their actions might *jeopardize* the outcome of the play.

Unit 4, Part 2 Answers

Benchmark Test 8, p. 197

MULTIPLE CHOICE
1. ANS: A
2. ANS: D
3. ANS: D
4. ANS: A

5. ANS: C

6. ANS: B

7. ANS: C

8. ANS: D

9. ANS: A

10. ANS: C

11. ANS: D

12. ANS: C

13. ANS: C

14. ANS: A

15. ANS: D

16. ANS: B

17. ANS: A

18. ANS: A

19. ANS: B

20. ANS: C

21. ANS: A

22. ANS: A

23. ANS: D

24. ANS: C

25. ANS: C

26. ANS: D

27. ANS: D

28. ANS: C

ESSAY

29. Students should decide on their criteria for evaluating the song and make their criteria clear in their essays. They should begin their essays with a concise statement that identifies the song and their opinion of it. They should provide examples and other details from the song to support general statements about it.

30. Students should use strong, precise images and figurative language in their poems. They should determine the mood they want to convey and use images, figurative language, and/or sound devices that contribute to that mood. They should also choose their words carefully to convey a tone and voice appropriate to the mood.

31. Students should include a thesis statement that clearly identifies the work and presents their personal response to it. They should refer to several elements in the work, such as characters, theme, plot, conflict, and setting, and they should provide details from the work to support general statements about it. They may include examples from other texts, opinions from literary scholars, or other outside ideas related to the work. Students should organize their responses in an effective and logical way and make them relatively free of grammar and other errors.